FUNGICIDES
FOR FIELD CROPS

Edited by

Daren S. Mueller
Iowa State University

Kiersten A. Wise
Purdue University

Nicholas S. Dufault
University of Florida–Gainesville

Carl A. Bradley
University of Illinois at Urbana–Champaign

Martin I. Chilvers
Michigan State University

APS
PRESS

The American Phytopathological Society
St. Paul, Minnesota

Art Credits

Front cover photos: Top and Bottom center: Courtesy Marcia McMullen; Middle left: Courtesy Tamra Jackson-Ziems; Middle center: Courtesy Scott Bretthauer; Middle right and Bottom right: Courtesy Daren S. Mueller; Bottom left: Courtesy Samuel Markell.

Interior photos: pages 1, 2, 16, 50, 88: Courtesy Daren S. Mueller; pages 4, 43, 44, 48, 61, 95: Courtesy Samuel Markell; page 10: Courtesy Kenneth Seebold; pages 15, 20, 29, 30, 72: Courtesy Marcia McMullen; pages 25, 54: Courtesy Tristan Mueller; pages 36, 81: Courtesy Kiersten A. Wise; page 64: Courtesy Nicholas S. Dufault; page 69: Courtesy Amanda J. Gevens; page 78: Courtesy Tom Allen; page 85: Courtesy Tamra Jackson-Ziems; page 92: Courtesy Mohamed Khan; page 98: Courtesy Kenneth Seebold. (Photo credits for numbered figures appear in place.)

Interior illustrations: pages 5, 6, 7, 8, 27: Courtesy Renée Tesdall.

The fungicide information provided in this publication is intended only as a general guide. By law, it is the responsibility of the fungicide user to read and follow all current label directions. Label restrictions and fungicide recommendations may be different in each state and country because of variations in disease status and recommended use. The references to fungicides and recommendations for management included in this publication are not intended as endorsements to the exclusion of others that may be similar. Persons using such products assume responsibility for their use in accordance with current manufacturers' directions. The authors and contributors assume no liability resulting from the use of these products or recommendations.

This publication includes general information for common diseases of field crops that may be managed with fungicides and other practices. Tables may not include all diseases for all crops.

Reference in this publication to a trademark, proprietary product, or company name by personnel of the U.S. Department of Agriculture or anyone else is intended for explicit description only and does not imply approval or recommendation to the exclusion of others that may be suitable.

Library of Congress Control Number: 2012945083
International Standard Book Number: 978-0-89054-420-4

© 2013 by The American Phytopathological Society

Printed in the United States of America on acid-free paper

The American Phytopathological Society
3340 Pilot Knob Road
St. Paul, Minnesota 55121, U.S.A.

Preface

Fungicides have been used in field crop production since the 1600s. Fungicide use was deemed revolutionary, however, by M. M. Tillet's discovery in 1755 that seedborne fungi, such as the pathogen that causes wheat bunt (*Tilletia tritici*), could be managed with applications of lime to seed. This discovery changed our ability to manage important and economically devastating diseases. Since those early days of plant pathology, our knowledge and use of fungicides have developed substantially, spanning from the use of inorganic chemicals to new uses of organic and synthetic fungicides.

The goal of this publication is to provide an overview of the current knowledge of fungicides and their use on field crops. It is a combination and expansion of two previous publications: *Field Crop Fungicides for the North Central United States* (Mueller and Bradley, 2008), developed by the North Central IPM Center and the Cooperative State Research, Education, and Extension Service (CSREES), and *Using Foliar Fungicides to Manage Soybean Rust* (Dorrance et al., 2007), developed by the North Central Education/Extension Research Activities committee (NCERA 208) and the Ontario Ministry of Agriculture, Food, and Rural Affairs (OMAFRA).

This new publication, *Fungicides for Field Crops*, combines past knowledge about fungicides with recent developments in the realm of field crop fungicides, such as the potential for development of fungicide resistance. In addition, it highlights the use of fungicides as key tools in the management of important diseases of field crops. However, this publication also focuses on the need to use fungicides

responsibly to preserve their effectiveness and to recognize their effects on both people and the environment. In the coming years, our goal should be to expand on the foundation of information provided in this publication, building on the available knowledge of fungicides as new issues and technology develop.

Approximately 40 professionals from 20 universities and other organizations contributed content, images, and recommendations to the development of this publication. The result is a comprehensive treatment of fungicide use across major field crops, with consideration given to fungicide use and recommendations for specific crops. This publication is not intended to provide an exhaustive list of fungicides for use in managing every disease present on field crops. Moreover, references to fungicide use are intended to serve only as a guide for readers and may not include all relevant work on fungicides in field crops.

Even so, the editors believe that the thorough and dedicated work put forth by all of the contributors has resulted in an invaluable and timely publication. It will provide current and future agronomists and farmers not only with useful baseline information but also crop-specific information about fungicide use.

Daren S. Mueller
Kiersten A. Wise
Nicholas S. Dufault
Carl A. Bradley
Martin I. Chilvers

Acknowledgments

Reviewers

Clayton Hollier, Louisiana State University
Douglas J. Jardine, Kansas State University
Edward Sikora, Auburn University
Adam Sisson, Iowa State University

Contributors

Alfalfa
Authors: Albert Tenuta, Ontario Ministry
of Agriculture, Food, and Rural Affairs,
and Craig Grau, University of Wisconsin–Madison
Reviewer: Paul Esker, University of Costa Rica

Canola
Author: Samuel Markell, North Dakota State
University
Reviewer: Carl A. Bradley, University of Illinois
at Urbana–Champaign

Corn
Authors: Carl A. Bradley, University of Illinois
at Urbana–Champaign; Daren S. Mueller, Iowa State
University; and Kiersten A. Wise, Purdue University

Cotton
Author: Robert C. Kemerait, University of Georgia
Reviewer: Kenneth Seebold, University of Kentucky

Dry Beans
Author: Robert Harveson, University
of Nebraska–Lincoln
Reviewers: Howard Schwartz, Colorado State
University, and Craig Grau, University
of Wisconsin–Madison

Flax
Author: Khalid Y. Rashid, Agriculture
and Agri-Food Canada
Reviewers: Carl A. Bradley, University of Illinois
at Urbana–Champaign, and Samuel Markell,
North Dakota State University

Peanut
Author: Robert C. Kemerait, University of Georgia
Reviewer: Nicholas S. Dufault, University
of Florida–Gainesville

Potato
Author: Amanda J. Gevens, University
of Wisconsin–Madison
Reviewer: Nicholas S. Dufault, University
of Florida–Gainesville

Pulse Crops
Author: Michael Wunsch, North Dakota State
University
Reviewer: Lyndon Porter, U.S. Department
of Agriculture, Prosser, Washington

Rice
Authors: Scott Monfort, Clemson University;
Donald Groth, Louisiana State University;
and Tom Allen, Mississippi State University
Reviewer: Richard D. Cartwright, University
of Arkansas

Small Grains
Authors: Erick De Wolfe, Kansas State University,
and Marcia McMullen, North Dakota State University

Sorghum
Author: Douglas J. Jardine, Kansas State University
Reviewer: Tamra Jackson-Ziems, University
of Nebraska–Lincoln

Soybean
Author: Daren S. Mueller, Iowa State University
Reviewer: Kiersten A. Wise, Purdue University

Sugar Beet
Author: Mohamed F. R. Khan, North Dakota State
University
Reviewer: Robert Harveson, University
of Nebraska–Lincoln

Sunflower
Author: Samuel Markell, North Dakota State
University
Reviewer: Robert Harveson, University
of Nebraska–Lincoln

Tobacco
Author: Kenneth Seebold, University of Kentucky
Reviewer: Nicholas S. Dufault, University
of Florida–Gainesville

Contents

Part I
Introduction

Fungicide Use

Fungicides are pesticides used to limit initial infection by and progress of plant pathogens and thus prevent damage to plants. Most fungicides are foliar or seed applied and used to protect the potential yield and quality of a crop.

The use of foliar-applied fungicides is common in many field crops—including peanut, potato, rice, and sugar beet—and use has recently increased in crops such as corn and soybean (Fig. 1). Foliar fungicides target fungi that infect the aboveground portions of plants. The majority of these fungicides protect foliage from infection; therefore, these fungicides should be applied before widespread infection develops on portions of the plant that contribute to yield. The decision to apply a foliar fungicide should be based on several factors, including weather conditions, disease status, application cost, physiological stage of the crop, and potential yield and market value of the crop.

Seed treatment fungicides are applied as a protective coating to seeds prior to planting (Fig. 2). They protect seeds from soilborne or seedborne fungi that cause rotting, damping-off, seedling blight, or a combination of these diseases. When seeds germinate under favorable soil conditions, they are less susceptible to soilborne diseases, unless they are of poor quality. Seed treatments may protect seedlings that germinate under unfavorable conditions, such as cold and wet weather, or when seeds are of poor quality, but seed treatments will not improve germination of poor-quality seed.

The recent increase in fungicide use in field crops is a result of a combination of several factors. Those factors include higher market prices for some crops, increased levels of disease, and the availability and marketing of new fungicides.

Higher Market Prices

Market prices for several crop commodities have increased dramatically since 2000 and particularly since 2007 (Table 1). Several factors have driven up prices to record highs over the last few years, including the expansion of global markets (particularly in Asia) and U.S. legislation that has supported alternative sources of fuel (such as ethanol and biofuels).

Increased Levels of Disease

Higher levels of disease in recent years have increased the need for disease management of some crops. Crop production practices such as reduced tillage and no-till cause an increase in the amount of crop residue, which can serve as a source of primary inoculum for several important foliar and soilborne diseases (Fig. 3). Changing weather patterns and pest pressure also affect crop growth and development

Fig. 1. A soybean field being treated with foliar fungicide. (Courtesy Daren S. Mueller)

Fig. 2. Corn seed treated with fungicide. (Courtesy Kiersten A. Wise)

(Hatfield et al., 2008). In recent years, concern has grown about outbreaks of several field crop diseases (Fig. 4), and researchers predict that leaf and root pathogens will be more problematic because of an overall increase in humidity and frequency of heavy rainfall events projected for many parts of the United States (Coakley et al., 1999).

Availability and Marketing of New Fungicides

There has been a dramatic increase in the number of both foliar- and seed-applied fungicides available for use on field crops. For example, in 2000, few foliar fungicides were available for soybean, but during the last decade, more than 30 fungicide products labeled for soybean have become available. Most of these newly available products belong in one of two classifications of fungicide: quinone outside inhibitors (QoIs), some of which are known as strobilurins, and demethylation inhibitors (DMIs), some of which are referred to as triazoles. Another recent change is that chemical companies now widely market fungicides for use in field crop production.

TABLE 1. Average prices of crop commodities (grains or products) from 2000–2006 and 2007–2010 (in U.S. dollars)[a]

Crop	2000–2006	2007–2010	Units
Alfalfa	$99.90	$133.50	tons
Barley	$2.53	$4.49	bushels
Corn	$2.24	$4.30	bushels
Cotton	$0.48	$0.65	pounds
Dry beans	$19.91	$29.85	cwt[b]
Flax	$5.58	$11.51	bushels
Oat	$1.57	$2.55	bushels
Peanut	$0.20	$0.22	pounds
Potato	$6.37	$8.51	cwt[b]
Rice	$6.77	$14.10	cwt[b]
Rye	$3.08	$5.38	bushels
Sorghum	$3.95	$7.14	cwt[b]
Soybean	$5.66	$10.34	bushels
Sugar beet	$39.94	$50.55	tons
Sunflower	$11.57	$20.00	cwt[b]
Tobacco	$1.87	$1.78	pounds
Wheat	$3.35	$5.96	bushels

[a] Data from U.S. Department of Agriculture (2007, 2010).
[b] cwt = centrum weight (100 pounds).

Fig. 3. Pathogens of many diseases can survive in the residue left on the soil surface. (Courtesy Greg Shaner)

Fig. 4. New diseases, such as soybean rust (top), and reemerging diseases, such as northern leaf blight on corn (bottom), are targets for fungicides. (Courtesy Daren S. Mueller)

Fungicide Terminology

Key Concepts

A **fungicide** is a chemical agent that kills or inhibits the growth of fungi or fungal-like organisms. A given fungicide can be referred to by at least three names, all of which can be found on the product label (Fig. 5):

chemical name: the name of the active ingredient in a fungicide (for example, carbamic acid, [2-[[[1-(4-chlorophenyl)-1H-pyrazol-3-yl]oxy]methyl]phenyl] methoxy-, methyl ester).

common name: the less technical name of the active ingredient (for example, pyraclostrobin).

trade name: the registered name under which the active ingredient is commercially available (for example, Headline). The active ingredient may be marketed under several different trade names.

Fig. 5. Identifying the information on a fungicide label. (Headline label courtesy BASF)

Classification Criteria

Fungicides can be classified according to a number of different criteria:

1. mobility in the plant
2. role in the protection of plants
3. breadth of metabolic activity
4. mode of action
5. chemical group or class
6. FRAC code

1. Mobility in the Plant

contact fungicide: a fungicide that remains on the surface of the plant where it is applied but is not absorbed into plant tissue. This type of fungicide has no postinfection activity. Repeated applications are needed to protect new growth of the plant and to replace fungicide that has been washed off by rain or irrigation or degraded by environmental factors such as sunlight.

systemic fungicide: a fungicide that moves into plant tissue and may offer some postinfection activity. Very few fungicides are truly systemic (moving freely throughout the plant). However, some are upwardly systemic (moving up in the plant through xylem tissue), and some are locally systemic (moving into treated leaves and redistributing somewhat within the treated portion of the plant) (Fig. 6).

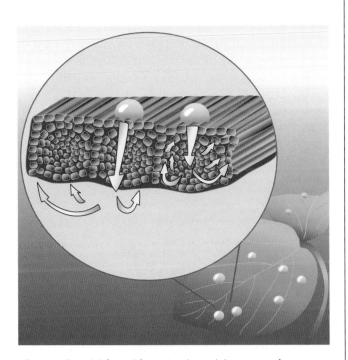

Fig. 6. Fungicides with systemic activity enter plant tissue and move within the plant (droplet on right); fungicides with translaminar activity move through the leaf from the sprayed surface to the nonsprayed surface (droplet on left). (Courtesy Iowa State University)

2. Role in the Protection of Plants[1]

preventive activity: occurs when a fungicide is present on the plant as a protective barrier before the pathogen arrives or begins to develop; that is, the fungicide prevents infection from occurring. (This type of activity is also referred to as **protective activity.**)

early infection activity: occurs when a fungicide is absorbed by the plant and stops the pathogen in its early developmental stages—usually within 24–72 hours after infection occurs, depending on the fungicide. (This type of activity is sometimes referred to as **curative** or **kickback activity.**) Most fungicides that have early infection activity also have preventive activity and are most effective when applied before infection occurs.

antisporulant activity: occurs when a fungicide prevents spores from being produced. In this case, disease continues to develop (for example, lesions continue to expand), but spores are not produced or released, so the amount of inoculum available to infect surrounding plants is reduced.

3. Breadth of Metabolic Activity

single-site fungicide: a fungicide that is active against only one point or function in one of the metabolic pathways of a fungus or against a single critical enzyme or protein needed by the fungus (Fig. 7). This type of fungicide tends to have systemic properties.

multisite fungicide: a fungicide that affects a number of different metabolic sites within the fungus (Fig. 7).

5. Mode of Action

A fungicide's **mode of action** is the means by which it kills or suppresses a target fungus or affects specific biochemical processes of the target fungus. Examples of modes of action include damaging cell membranes,

---

[1] Some fungicides demonstrate more than one of these types of activity.

inactivating critical enzymes or proteins, and interfering with key processes, such as energy production and respiration.

5. Chemical Group or Class

A **chemical group** or **class** is a set of chemicals that have a common biochemical mode of action and may or may not have a similar chemical structure. Fungicides approved for use on field crops fall into different chemical groups.

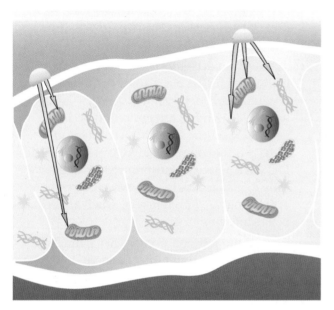

Fig. 7. Fungicides can affect a single site (droplet on left) or multiple sites (droplet on right) of a fungus. (Courtesy Iowa State University)

6. FRAC Code

The Fungicide Resistance Action Committee (FRAC) is an organization developed to address the issue of fungicide resistance. This organization developed a code of numbers and letters that is used to distinguish different fungicide groups based on their modes of action. This code is known as the **FRAC code** (see Table 2 for examples). (FRAC codes are discussed in more detail in Part III.)

Additional Terms

active ingredient (a.i.): the molecule that provides biological activity to control the fungus.

adjuvant: a compound that is tank mixed or included in the pesticide formulation to improve coverage on the plant or penetration into leaf tissue. Adjuvants are also known as **spreader-stickers** and **surfactants.**

baseline sensitivity: the amount of fungicide that is able to effectively control a fungal plant pathogen population that has never been exposed to the fungicide.

biological fungicide (biofungicide): a fungicide that is composed of living organisms or their metabolites (such as antibiotics).

chemigation: application of a fungicide through a sprinkler irrigation system (Fig. 8). Chemigation is referred to as **fungigation** on some fungicide labels.

TABLE 2. Examples of field crop fungicides with different classifications			
	Trade Name(s)		
Properties	**Headline**	**Proline**	**Manzate, Dithane, and Penncozeb**
Active ingredient	Pyraclostrobin	Prothioconazole	Mancozeb
FRAC code	11	3	M
Chemical group or class	Methoxycarbamate (strobilurin)	Triazole	Dithiocarbamates and relatives
Mode of action	Quinone outside inhibitor (QoI)	Demethylation inhibitor (DMI)	Multisite contact activity
Mobility in plant	Locally systemic	Upwardly systemic	Contact
Role in protection	Protectant and early infection for some pathogens	Protectant and early infection	Protectant
Breadth of activity	Single site	Single site	Multisite

Fig. 8. A center-pivot chemigation application made to potato. (Courtesy Lyndon Porter)

cross-resistance: when a fungus becomes resistant to more than one fungicide within a FRAC code.

fungicide resistance: the reduction in sensitivity to a fungicide by an individual fungus. Fungicides with single-site modes of action are at relatively high risk for developing resistance compared to those with multisite modes of action.

in-furrow: refers to a fungicide applied in the seeding furrow of the targeted crop, usually at planting.

integrated pest management (IPM): an approach that uses a combination of management strategies to reduce yield loss from pests.

monocyclic: refers to a pathogen having only one life cycle in a growing season (Fig. 9).

Fig. 9. White mold of soybean is an example of a disease with a monocyclic life cycle. (Courtesy Iowa State University)

pathogen: an organism that causes disease. Pathogens include fungi, fungal-like organisms (for example, oomycetes, such as *Phytophthora* and *Pythium* species), bacteria, viruses, and nematodes.

phytotoxicity: the condition in which plant tissue has been damaged by a chemical.

polycyclic: refers to a pathogen having multiple life cycles in a growing season. Fungal pathogens with multiple life cycles are often referred to as having repeating spore stages (Fig. 10).

preharvest interval (PHI): the minimum amount of time that must pass between the last pesticide application and harvesting of the crop or grazing or cutting it for livestock feed. Typically, PHIs for fungicides applied to field crops range from 7 to 30 days, depending on the crop and the fungicide. Some fungicides have restrictions based on crop growth stages instead of a specific number of days.

reduced-risk fungicide: a fungicide that has less negative impact on humans and the environment, as well as lower potential for accumulation in groundwater, than other fungicides. Many biological fungicides are reduced-risk fungicides.

Fig. 10. Gray leaf spot of corn is an example of a disease with a polycyclic life cycle. The disease cycle repeats throughout the season, and disease progresses up the plant. During the repeating life cycles, infected leaves become the source of inoculum, rather than corn residue. (Courtesy Iowa State University)

restricted entry interval (REI): the minimum time between application of a pesticide to a field and when it is safe to reenter that field. All agricultural pesticides labeled after April 1994 are required to have an REI stated on the label. REIs for fungicides, like those for other pesticides, are established to reduce pesticide exposure and are based on product toxicity. REIs range from 12 to 24 hours for most fungicides. Workers should not enter a treated area until the REI has passed.

restricted use product (RUP): a pesticide that can be bought and handled only by a licensed, certified pesticide applicator or under the supervision of a certified pesticide applicator.

translaminar: a type of activity in which the fungicide is redistributed from the sprayed leaf surface, through the leaf, to the unsprayed leaf surface (that is, it moves from the top of a sprayed leaf to its underside) (Fig. 6, page 5).

Fungicide Application

Foliar Fungicides

Foliar fungicides can be applied using ground, aerial, or irrigation (chemigation) application equipment:

- Ground applicators apply fungicides in a similar way as other foliar-applied chemicals (Fig. 11).
- Aerially applied fungicides are applied at a reduced volume per acre and may require an adjuvant to force the chemical down into the canopy of the crop (Fig. 12). Several types of aircraft can apply fungicides, and farmers should work with aerial applicators to ensure that adequate coverage of the target crop is achieved.

- Irrigation distribution systems generally have the capability of applying fungicides—especially systems that are highly sophisticated. Center-pivot and linear systems are the most common irrigation systems used for chemigation.

In general, the basic factors involved in applying foliar fungicides are similar to those for applying other foliar pesticides (such as insecticides). Application method, droplet size, nozzle type, operating pressure, volume of water, and formulation can all influence fungicide efficacy.

Fig. 12. Aerial application of foliar fungicide. (Courtesy Scott Bretthauer)

Fig. 11. Ground application of fungicides is similar to that of other foliar-applied chemicals. (Courtesy Greg Shaner)

Key Factors in Applying Foliar Fungicides

1. Fungicide nozzles and spray pressures should be selected to produce a droplet size of 200–300 microns (Fig. 13). This is typically a smaller droplet than what is recommended for herbicide application.

2. Fungicide mobility is generally limited in plants, so adequate carrier volume is important for spray coverage. Higher volumes may be necessary as crops grow and plant density increases.

3. Some plant surfaces have a waxy or hairy coating that will cause fungicides to collect in large droplets, which run off the plant surface and thus reduce fungicide coverage (Fig. 14). Using a wetting agent, such as an adjuvant or surfactant, will improve coverage. However, some surfactants can cause plant damage if applied incorrectly or at the wrong stage of plant growth. Information on the correct use of surfactants can usually be found on products' labels or in supplemental brochures. Adjuvants are usually included in flowable-type fungicide formulations, so adding an adjuvant to a fungicide in this form is not necessary and may in fact be detrimental to the fungicide's performance.

4. Fungicide penetration in the lower canopy may be necessary to achieve optimal performance. Using a special nozzle, such as a drop nozzle or angled nozzle, can improve coverage.

5. Fungicide efficacy is maximized when application is made under ideal environmental conditions. Individual and systemwide spray capacity limitations may make it necessary to spray some fields under less than ideal conditions.

6. Preharvest intervals may limit choices of fungicides later in the season.

Fig. 13. Using different nozzles to apply fungicides can affect the size of the spray droplets. (Courtesy Tristan Mueller)

Fig. 14. Fungicide coverage can be reduced by plant surfaces with a hairy or waxy coating. (Courtesy Nicholas S. Dufault)

Seed Treatments

Fungicide seed treatments for field crops are used primarily for three reasons:

1. to manage soilborne pathogens that cause seed rots, damping-off, seedling blights, and root rot
2. to manage pathogens that are surface borne on the seed, such as those that cause covered smuts of barley and oats, common bunt of wheat, seedborne safflower rust, and downy mildew of soybean
3. to internally manage seedborne pathogens, such as the loose smut fungi of cereals (McMullen and Lamey, 2000)

Seed treatment recommendations, usage, and availability are extremely crop specific (Fig. 15). For example, almost all commercial hybrid corn, sugar beet, and canola seed is pretreated with at least one fungicide mode of action. Treating seed is not always economical in other field crops, such as wheat and soybean, although seed treatment is beneficial in specific areas and conditions. Seed treatment efficacy will depend on the choice of product, application method, application rate, planting method, soil type, soil conditions (both at and immediately after planting), and field history and level of disease.

Economic factors should also be considered, since treating seed with fungicide will add to the production cost.

Seed may be treated commercially or on the farm (Fig. 16). Commercial seed treatment is becoming a standard practice for many field crops, including wheat and soybean, because of the precision required to treat each seed with the appropriate formulation of active ingredients. Commercial facilities may also have the ability to use direct-injection methods to coat or pellet the seed with the treatment, which is more efficient than the simple seed-dressing process done on the farm or with slurry seed treatment equipment. The key advantage of direct-injection methods is that they optimize the amount of active ingredient on each seed. Coating or pelleting the seed can improve seed treatment adherence and seed uniformity, which aids in planting. In addition, commercial seed treatment eliminates many of the health and handling risks of on-farm treatment. This practice is also becoming more common as many fungicide seed treatments are packaged as combination products with insecticides and nematicides that are restricted use products (RUPs). An RUP can be handled only by a certified pesticide applicator or under the supervision of a certified pesticide applicator. Fungicide seed treatments can be detrimental to seed inoculants (nitrogen-fixing bacteria),

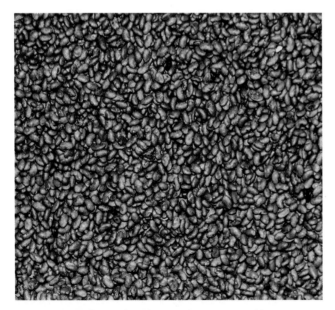

Fig. 15. Alfalfa seed with a seed treatment. (Courtesy Adam Sisson)

Fig. 16. Treating peanut seed before planting. (Courtesy Nicholas S. Dufault)

so care should be exercised when both are being used. Farmers should refer to product labels for precautions and mixing instructions.

Although less common than commercial seed treatment, on-farm seed dressing is still possible with the use of drill-box seed treaters and slurry mixers. Another common on-farm method is to add a liquid fungicide seed treatment into the base of the auger used to fill the drill box. These methods are easy and convenient but may not ensure accurate coverage of the seed. They may also require additional worker protection, such as gloves and a chemical respirator, depending on the product and formulation. Many logistical considerations are also involved with these applications, and it is important to avoid mechanical damage to the seed.

Other Types of Application

Other types of application may be available for certain fungicides, including banding and in-furrow applications. These types may require special equipment or modifications to current equipment. The product label for a given fungicide should be checked carefully to see whether these application options are available.

Part II
Decision-Making Factors for Fungicide Use

Decision-Making Process for Applying a Foliar Fungicide

To ensure success, the decision to apply a fungicide to a field crop should be based on several factors. The farmer or applicator should consider economics, field production practices, weather conditions (both before and after the crop enters a vulnerable growth stage), and the present or potential risk for disease. The greatest chance of success comes when a fungicide is applied to prevent yield loss in a field at high risk for disease. A farmer who applies a fungicide in a low-risk or low-disease environment must manage expectations about the profitability of that application.

Key Factors

Economics

Economic factors must be considered in the decision-making process for fungicide application. Those factors include the market price of the crop and the costs of application, including labor, machinery, fuel, and fungicide materials. As mentioned previously, crop prices have increased dramatically since 2005.

TABLE 3. Average custom applicator costs for spraying corn and soybean: 2000 and 2011, Iowa (in U.S. dollars)[a,b]

Application Type	2000	2011
Ground, broadcast	$4.30/acre ($10.62/ha)	$6.80/acre ($16.80/ha)
Aerial	$5.25/acre ($12.97/ha)	$8.90/acre ($21.98/ha)

[a] Data from Edwards et al. (2000, 2011).
[b] Costs do not include the cost of spray material.

However, the cost of application for several crops has also increased 60–70% since that time (Table 3).

Environmental factors can influence disease development, and potential yield losses from disease should be calculated to determine if fungicide application is warranted. In cases in which fungicides are used for benefits other than disease control or are used as insurance against potential disease threats, farmers must at least recoup the investment of the fungicide application to break even. This break-even point will fluctuate from year to year based on the market price of the crop and the costs of application. Examples of the break-even costs for corn are provided in Table 4.

Disease Severity and Risk

For many crops, the decision to apply a fungicide can be based on the presence of disease prior to the application. Making this decision must be specific to the disease and the crop. However, some diseases can be managed only by applying a fungicide before seeing visible symptoms on the crop.

To understand what diseases may be problematic, it is important to know the disease risk factors present in the field and the upcoming weather conditions. Having this information will help determine if preventive applications are required (for example, for white mold of soybean) (Fig. 17) or if scouting and thresholds can be used to aid in the decision-making process for fungicide application (for example, for rust on sunflower) (Fig. 18). Thresholds do not exist for every crop–disease combination, so it is important to contact local extension service personnel to get the

Fig. 17. Preventive fungicide applications work best for diseases such as white mold on soybean. (Courtesy Daren S. Mueller)

TABLE 4. Yields needed to equal the application cost of fungicide based on the price of corn

Price of Corn (U.S. dollars)	Application Cost[a] (U.S. dollars)			
	$20.00/acre ($49.40/ha)	$24.00/acre ($59.28/ha)	$28.00/acre ($69.16/ha)	$32.00/acre ($79.04/ha)
$2.00/bushel ($0.08/kg)	10.0 bushels/acre (628.7 kg/ha)	12.0 bushels/acre (754.5 kg/ha)	14.0 bushels/acre (880.2 kg/ha)	16.0 bushels/acre (1,006.0 kg/ha)
$3.00/bushel ($0.12/kg)	6.7 bushels/acre (421.2 kg/ha)	8.0 bushels/acre (503.0 kg/ha)	9.3 bushels/acre (584.7 kg/ha)	10.7 bushels/acre (672.7 kg/ha)
$4.00/bushel ($0.16/kg)	5.0 bushels/acre (314.4 kg/ha)	6.0 bushels/acre (377.2 kg/ha)	7.0 bushels/acre (440.1 kg/ha)	8.0 bushels/acre (503.0 kg/ha)
$5.00/bushel ($0.20/kg)	4.0 bushels/acre (251.5 kg/ha)	4.8 bushels/acre (301.8 kg/ha)	5.6 bushels/acre (352.1 kg/ha)	6.4 bushels/acre (402.4 kg/ha)
$6.00/bushel ($0.24/kg)	3.3 bushels/acre (207.5 kg/ha)	4.0 bushels/acre (251.5 kg/ha)	4.7 bushels/acre (295.5 kg/ha)	5.3 bushels/acre (333.2 kg/ha)
$7.00/bushel ($0.28/kg)	2.9 bushels/acre (182.3 kg/ha)	3.4 bushels/acre (213.8 kg/ha)	4.0 bushels/acre (251.5 kg/ha)	4.6 bushels/acre (289.2 kg/ha)
$8.00/bushel ($0.31/kg)	2.5 bushels/acre (157.2 kg/ha)	3.0 bushels/acre (188.6 kg/ha)	3.5 bushels/acre (220.1 kg/ha)	4.0 bushels/acre (251.5 kg/ha)

[a] Includes cost of product.

latest information on disease thresholds for the crop of interest.

Numerous research trials have shown that the greatest benefit from fungicide applications to field crops occurs when fungicides are used in response to the presence of disease or to an immediate threat of disease. Certain fields and crops are more likely to develop disease based on particular risk factors, and the risk of disease increases for each factor that is present in a single field. Priority for disease management should be given to fields with the highest number of factors that favor disease development.

Factors That Increase the Risk of Disease Development

Cultivar Selection

Crop breeders emphasize incorporating genetic resistance to common diseases into commercial cultivars, but not all cultivars are resistant to all diseases (Fig. 19).

Fig. 18. Timing of fungicide applications for some diseases, such as rust on sunflower, can be based on thresholds. (Courtesy Andrew Friskop)

Fig. 19. Tobacco plants that are resistant (left) and susceptible (right) to black shank. (Courtesy Kenneth Seebold)

Scouting for Disease

The best ways to determine if a fungicide application is necessary are (1) to be aware of the diseases that affect crops regionally or even nationally and (2) to scout fields regularly (Fig. 20). Awareness of key issues and risks for disease development during the growing season will aid in the decision-making process for applying a fungicide. Extension personnel frequently report on current trends and disease issues during the growing season in newsletters and online posts.

Knowing what diseases are present in neighboring counties or states may provide a starting point for knowing what to look for when scouting. Scouting allows farmers to decide whether fungicides are needed and, if they are, when they should be applied to target the stage at which the crop is most vulnerable to economic loss. Applications timed to protect the crop during this window of opportunity are often more profitable than applications scheduled too early or too late.

Scouting will also help develop field disease histories for individual fields, which can be used for future management.

Fig. 20. Farmers should scout regularly and stay informed of local disease and weather conditions. (Courtesy Marcia McMullen)

Knowing the inherent susceptibility of a given cultivar to common root diseases may affect the decision to use a seed treatment and perhaps what seed treatment to use. Similarly, if a cultivar is susceptible to a foliar disease, the risk of that disease developing will increase if environmental conditions are favorable, thus increasing the likelihood that application of a foliar fungicide will be necessary.

Production Practices and Inoculum Level

Conservation tillage prevents soil erosion and conserves soil moisture. However, this practice leaves crop residue on the soil surface after harvest, providing food and habitat for certain plant pathogens. Infested crop residue is an important inoculum source and may increase the likelihood of disease developing. Continuous cropping or rotating to crops susceptible to the same pathogen will also increase the amount of crop residue that can harbor pathogens and thus increase inoculum. Fields with short crop rotations or reduced tillage are at higher risk for the development of disease (Fig. 21).

Fig. 21. Corn seedlings growing through corn residue from the previous year. (Courtesy Kiersten A. Wise)

Environment

Environment and weather play a critical role in the process of fungal infection and disease development. For example, the development of many foliar diseases is favored by rainy and humid weather (Fig. 22). In growing seasons when these conditions prevail, the risk for disease development increases. Conversely, even when other risk factors for disease are present, unfavorable weather conditions for a given fungus will prevent infection from occurring or limit disease development in a crop. In some instances, predictive models are available to aid in assessing the weather conditions prior to fungicide application and can be used to help determine whether an application is justified.

Some fields have a history of high disease severity, which can influence the need for a fungicide application. Fields in river bottoms, low areas, and sections surrounded by trees may be more prone to developing foliar diseases, whereas fields with heavy, compacted soil and poor drainage are more prone to developing certain soilborne diseases.

Some management practices—including adjustments to the planting date, row spacing, and plant population—may affect the environment in which the crop grows, which can in turn affect disease development. Also, irrigated fields have a higher risk for certain diseases, since free moisture on plant tissue and wet soils create a more conducive environment for disease development (Fig. 23).

Fig. 22. Foliar disease development can be favored by rainy or humid weather. (Courtesy Daren S. Mueller)

Fig. 23. Moisture on plant tissue creates a more conducive environment for disease development. (Courtesy Tamra Jackson-Ziems)

Factors in the Success or Failure of Foliar Fungicide Application

Many factors may affect the success of a foliar fungicide application. Decisions made before or during the application can affect the response to the fungicide, and the environmental conditions present during and after the application also can affect the outcome. The following sections address possible factors in the success or failure of a fungicide application.

Preapplication Factors

Lack of Yield-Limiting Disease

Some fungicides are applied in the absence of significant disease pressure or disease threat. Research indicates that foliar fungicide applications made in low-disease environments may not result in economic yield increases. Additionally, preventive applications may not be profitable if the disease does not develop because of unfavorable weather conditions following application.

For example, the response to foliar fungicides applied to corn varies depending on the disease level. Fungicide applications increased yield by almost 10 bushels per acre (629 kg/ha) when disease severity was greater than 5% on the ear leaf at the early dent stage of corn development. In contrast, yield returns from fungicide applications averaged less than 2 bushels per acre (126 kg/ha) when disease severity was below 5% at the same stage of development (Table 5).

Moreover, not all of the diseases present on a plant may be of economic consequence. Some diseases are common yet rarely cause yield loss. Examples include common rust on corn and peanut and brown spot on potato and soybean (Fig. 24).

Fig. 24. Some diseases, such as brown spot on soybean, are common yet rarely cause yield loss. (Courtesy Daren S. Mueller)

TABLE 5. Corn yield response to quinone outside inhibitor (QoI) fungicides: 2008–2010[a,b]

Disease Severity of Untreated Crop	Mean Yield Response	Total Treatments	Treatments with Break-Even Yield Response[c]
<5%	1.5 bushels/acre (94.4 kg/ha)	347	31.6%
>5%	9.6 bushels/acre (603.8 kg/ha)	266	59.0%

[a] Used with permission from Wise and Mueller (2011).
[b] Data are pooled across all treatments that included a QoI mode of action and were applied between V15 and R3 growth stages. Data include only trials for which disease severity ratings were submitted.
[c] Break-even yield response = 6.0 bushels/acre (377.4 kg/ha).

Incorrect Diagnosis

One reason for foliar fungicide failure is inaccurate disease diagnosis. With an incorrect diagnosis, a fungicide may be selected that does not manage the targeted disease. Common problems that may be mis-identified as fungal diseases include insect damage, chemical injury, bacterial disease, root damage from nematodes, genetically induced leaf spots, and environmental damage (Fig. 25).

Fungicide Selection

Even if the problem is accurately diagnosed as a fungal disease, foliar fungicides do not manage all fungal diseases or vary in the level of efficacy with which they control specific diseases. Product labels specify the disease organisms that may be managed by particular fungicides, and resources from extension services are available to help select the fungicides that are most effective against certain diseases.

Fungicide Storage

Maintaining proper storage conditions is important, because outdated or improperly stored fungicide materials may lose their activity and fail to work (Fig. 26). Fungicides stored longer than 2 years or under improper conditions (such as extreme cold) may lose their activity. Some flowable fungicides tend to settle out in containers over time (Fig. 27). To help ensure the proper dosage of active ingredient, container contents must be mixed thoroughly before dispensing the fungicide into the sprayer.

Fig. 26. Maintaining proper storage conditions is important for ensuring fungicide viability. (Courtesy Nicholas S. Dufault)

Fig. 25. Disease look-alikes, such as herbicide injury (top) and physiological symptoms (bottom), make correct diagnosis important. (Courtesy Kiersten A. Wise)

Fig. 27. Some flowable fungicides tend to settle out in containers over time. (Courtesy Kiersten A. Wise)

Factors During the Spraying Process

Fungicide Rates

Fungicides should be used at the recommended rates for effective disease management. Product labels may list a range of rates, and a specific recommended rate may be available that falls within this range. These rates or ranges are based on multiple-year and multiple-location testing to establish the most effective amount of product to use under a wide variety of environmental conditions. Given this, recommended rates may vary based on the disease or geographic location. Applying a fungicide below the recommended rate may result in inadequate disease control in some situations and possibly the development of resistant strains of the pathogen.

Proper Mixing

The treatment area and the amount of product to add to the mixing tank should be carefully calculated. Errors in calculation can result in ineffective disease control, damage to crops, and excessive fungicide costs.

Mixing fungicides with water that is too acidic or too alkaline can reduce fungicidal activity, especially for water with a pH greater than 8. Ideally, water with a pH near 7 should be used for mixing pesticides. If water pH is not favorable, it can be corrected with pH buffers, which are added to the water before mixing in fungicides.

Mixing multiple pesticides in a spray tank can save time, but the compatibility of the products should be tested. Incompatibility can result in the formation of insoluble precipitates in the spray tank. Product labels often contain information on mixing compatibility. If a label does not address compatibility, a small volume of the spray mix should be tested in a glass jar for 30 minutes; separation or settling of pesticides in the jar indicates incompatibility.

Fungicides begin to lose their activity if they sit too long in the spray tank. Fungicide activity often declines within 12 hours after mixing, and this process is accelerated by poor water quality (for instance, sediment, high or low pH).

Sprayer Calibration and Application

The most common cause of foliar fungicide application failure is likely incorrect sprayer calibration. If a sprayer is not properly calibrated, too much or too little fungicide can be applied, resulting in plant injury or poor disease management. To avoid these problems, sprayers should be recalibrated after any modification to the nozzle, pressure, or speed (Fig. 28). Calibrating and adjusting a sprayer takes time and effort, but doing so can save money and make fungicide applications more effective.

Order for Adding Formulations

The order in which pesticides of different formulations are added to the tank can affect compatibility. Different formulations should be added to the tank in the following order:

1. activators or compatibility agents
2. wettable powders (WP) and dry flowables (DF)
3. water-soluble concentrates (WSC or SC)
4. emulsifiable concentrates (EC)
5. soluble powders (SP)
6. adjuvants or spray additives

Fig. 28. Sprayers should be properly calibrated before use. (Courtesy Tristan Mueller)

Fungicides should be applied in the recommended volume of water, as well as at a constant speed and at the recommended pressure. Spray pressure should be adjusted for the type of nozzle used. It is important to note that the recommended pressures for fungicide applications are often different from the recommended pressures for herbicides. When preparing to apply a fungicide with equipment that is used to apply both herbicides and fungicides, the applicator should verify that the pressure and nozzle have been adjusted to optimize fungicide application. Excessively high sprayer pressure produces small droplets (less than 100 microns), which may drift from the targeted area. To avoid sprayer misses or overlap between field passes, boom width and height must be measured carefully and drive rows must be adjusted.

Application Timing

Avoiding yield loss requires applying fungicides at an appropriate time to limit disease development. Foliar fungicides typically have 14–21 days of activity, so they must be applied at the correct growth stage and prior to or at the onset of disease to maximize efficiency.

The application window varies by crop and disease, and in some instances, only a narrow window may be available for the fungicide to be effective. Examples include the wheat disease Fusarium head blight (Fig. 29) and the soybean disease white mold. In each case, a specific growth stage must be protected, and applications that are not made at that stage will be less effective or ineffective. Fungicides that are applied too early may break down prior to disease development or not provide coverage on new growth that requires protection. Fungicides that are applied after diseases can easily be found may not provide satisfactory or economical disease control.

Environmental Considerations

Environmental conditions during or immediately after foliar fungicide applications influence the final outcome. Applications made when temperatures exceed 90°F (32°C) and when humidity is low (less than 50%) may result in excessive evaporation of small droplets as they leave the nozzle. Also, spraying during windy conditions decreases efficacy because of product drift from the targeted area.

Foliage should be dry at the time fungicides are applied, as dew or rain on foliage can cause the product to become diluted or run off. Rain or irrigation within a few hours after application may wash off some product; fungicides differ in how quickly they become rainfast. A general rule for the amount of time needed between application and a rainfall event is that systemic fungicides need a minimum of 3 hours to dry on the plant surface. Contact fungicides are always sensitive to rain removal but more so before drying occurs on plant surfaces.

Postapplication Factors

Resistance

Fungicide resistance is a cause of fungicide failure but not the most likely reason a fungicide fails to control a disease. The only way to be certain of the presence of a fungicide-resistant pathogen in the field is to have the pathogen tested in a qualified lab. (A more complete discussion of fungicide resistance is provided in Part III.)

Phytotoxicity

Excess rates of fungicides and applications of fungicides under extreme environmental conditions can burn leaves or stunt plants in some field crops. Phytotoxicity can be avoided by applying fungicides at the recommended rates and according to label directions. Fungicides applied during hot weather can cause plant damage, in some instances.

Fig. 29. Fungicides should be applied at the appropriate time to maximize effectiveness, especially for diseases such as Fusarium head blight. (Courtesy Marcia McMullen)

The additives included in fungicide applications can also cause damage in field crops that is sometimes perceived as fungicide failure. A recent example of this is arrested ear development in corn (Fig. 30), which has been linked to pretassel applications of

Fig. 30. Arrested ear syndrome on corn caused by additives for foliar applications. (Courtesy Nathan Stetzel)

nonionic surfactants. Fungicide and additive product labels must be checked before application to determine the proper rates and uses of additives.

Field Variability

In some cases, farmers may feel that fungicides have failed, because yields of treated areas or fields are not higher than those of untreated areas or fields. This lack of perceived success occurs most frequently in fields with greater spatial variability and when disease severity is minimal. When natural variability in a field is greater than the expected yield response, it is difficult to sort out small yield responses or perceived yield losses caused by fungicide application.

The discrepancy in corn yield responses in low- and high-disease environments (Table 5, page 20) exemplifies how difficult it is to identify a small yield response if the spatial variability of a particular field exceeds 2 bushels per acre (126 kg/ha), which is the average yield response when foliar disease severity is low. If variability in a field is much greater than that, then the perception may be that fungicide application has caused a yield loss, depending on where the treated areas lie within the field.

Conducting On-Farm Comparisons to Test Fungicides

Conducting on-farm trials is a key component in validating the effectiveness of fungicide applications. This research may be conducted independently, at university agricultural experiment stations, or in everyday farm operations.

On-farm trials are different from small-plot research trials in several ways. Conducting trials using small plots allows researchers to examine many products or product uses (such as timings, rates, etc.) over a relatively uniform field area (Fig. 31). In contrast, conducting on-farm trials tests products using larger plots, which may affect trial uniformity. However, proper trial design can minimize the errors associated with larger plot trials and allow farmers to determine differences among treatments.

Steps in Developing an On-Farm Trial

Developing an on-farm trial involves following these basic steps:

1. Establish the trial goals and objectives.
2. Determine the treatments.
3. Assess the need for an untreated check or control plot.
4. Select a site and gather its history.
5. Determine the plot layout.
6. Determine what data will be collected.
7. Determine how the data will be evaluated.

Including an Untreated Check or Control Plot

On-farm trials are often designed to compare the effectiveness of a new fungicide with a currently used product. However, to make a true assessment of effectiveness requires measuring the amount of disease that would have been present had the fungicide not been used.

An untreated check or control plot is an essential part of university experiments, but its use in larger field plots is viewed as more difficult. Regardless, an untreated check should be included as another treatment in the experimental setup. The untreated check plot must be the same dimensions as the other treatment plots, and the check must be replicated and randomized within the other treatments to determine the fungicide's effectiveness in the trial.

Fig. 31. Plots for evaluation of soybean rust fungicide in Florida. (Courtesy Tristan Mueller)

Considerations for Conducting an On-Farm Trial

Key considerations for conducting an on-farm trial are as follow:

- Select a field site that is as uniform as possible. Avoid sections with hills or low-lying areas.
- Plan for at least three replications at each farm site.
- Determine what equipment is needed and available, and then design the trial accordingly.
- Calibrate the equipment before treatment application and harvest.
- Avoid fungicide treatment overlap by harvesting and taking data from the center of the plot.
- Take appropriate notes and photographs throughout the experiment.
- Stay in regular contact with researchers or farmers to avoid miscommunication.

Using Statistics to Interpret Experimental Results

Every on-farm trial will have a certain amount of experimental error because of environmental factors (such as differences in soil, topography, field history, etc.) that are beyond researchers' control (Fig. 32). The use of statistics allows researchers to determine how much error is present in the experiment and whether differences exist among treatments after accounting for this error.

Unfortunately, error cannot be estimated from a single plot, which is why treatments must be replicated within a field site. It is also important to assign treatments to plots randomly to be sure that estimates of error are not biased by underlying field conditions. Examples of improperly and properly randomized and replicated on-farm trials are shown in Figures 33 and 34, respectively.

The calculated experimental error in a properly conducted (replicated and randomized) on-farm trial is used to assess whether significant differences exist among treatments. This significance is based on probability and is usually referred to as a P value. The level of probability that defines significance is selected by the person conducting the experiment. The preferred level set by the scientific community is 90 or 95%. This means that to state with a 90% level of confidence that the differences observed among individual treatments resulted from the treatment itself (and not by chance), the P value is set at 0.10, or 10% (100% – 90%).

Fig. 32. Differences within a field can be causes of experimental error. (Courtesy Michael Wunsch)

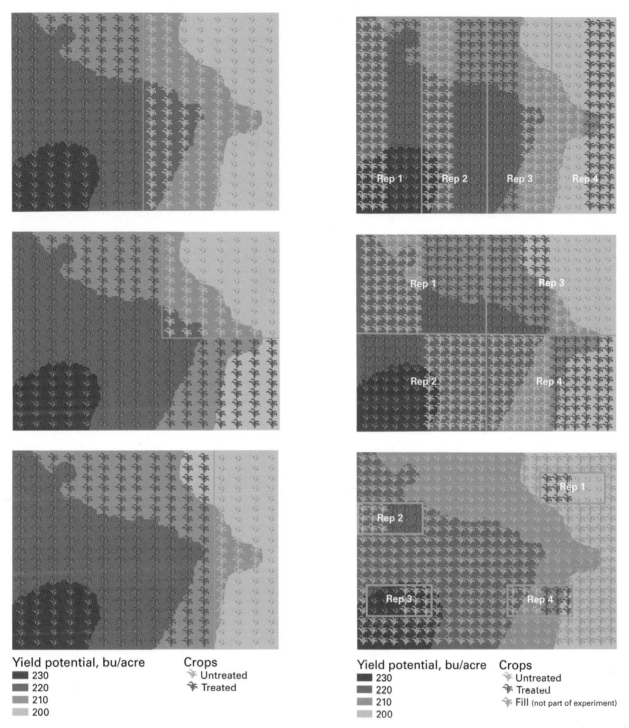

Yield potential, bu/acre
- 230
- 220
- 210
- 200

Crops
- ☘ Untreated
- ☘ Treated

Yield potential, bu/acre
- 230
- 220
- 210
- 200

Crops
- ☘ Untreated
- ☘ Treated
- ☘ Fill (not part of experiment)

Fig. 33. Examples of on-farm field designs that contain common design mistakes. These mistakes include lack of replication (top) and variation in plot sizes (middle and bottom) and do not account for the natural variation (yield potential) in the field that can bias the results. Making these mistakes can result in drawing conclusions that are incorrect or unfounded. (Courtesy Iowa State University)

Fig. 34. Examples of on-farm field designs that have proper replication and randomization. Each replication (Rep) must contain all of the treatments (treated and untreated) that are being examined in the test and should be equal in size. Treatments are to be randomly assigned to plots within the replication. Replications should be placed within the field to account for other factors influencing yield (such as soil fertility, moisture, etc.). This can be done by placing the replications in strips (top), quadrants (middle), or randomly (bottom) throughout the field site. (Courtesy Iowa State University)

To compare individual averages among treatments with equal numbers of replication, researchers use a comparison method called the **least significant difference (LSD)**. The LSD value is the smallest allowable difference between two treatment averages that can occur for them to be considered statistically different. Thus, the difference between the averages of two treatment values must be greater than or equal to the LSD value for it to be considered significant. For example, if the LSD value is 10, then the average yield between the two treatments must vary by 10 units or more for the difference to be considered statistically different. Otherwise, no statistical difference is observed between the treatments, and they can be considered as having the same effect, even if the averages are not the same.

The use of statistics provides researchers with a tool to explain and analyze errors associated with on-farm trials that cannot be controlled. Accounting for these errors allows researchers to evaluate whether differences exist among treatments. Thus, using statistics allows drawing meaningful conclusions about fungicide products that may be beneficial to agricultural production systems.

Part III
Fungicide Stewardship

Fungicide Resistance and the FRAC Code

Fungicide Resistance

Fungicides have been used on field crops since the 1700s (Morton and Staub, 2008). In the 1800s, fungicides were sulfur and copper based. Mercury fungicides were developed in the early 1900s and used widely until it was discovered that they were highly toxic to animals. In the 1940s and 1950s, fungicides such as captan and mancozeb were introduced. These contact fungicides worked only if applied before infection occurred. In addition, they affected several different biochemical sites within the fungus, so fungicide resistance did not readily appear.

More recently, highly effective fungicides with very specific modes of action have been developed, such as the quinone outside inhibitors (QoIs). These products generally have several attractive properties, including being more systemic than contact fungicides while still managing a broad range of fungal pathogens. However, since these fungicides affect one specific site or function in one metabolic pathway of the pathogen, the fungus only has one barrier or one change in site or function to overcome the product's action. Thus, the problem of fungicide resistance has emerged and continues to increase, because farmers rely more and more on these newer fungicides.

Development of fungicide resistance is a worldwide concern for the agricultural industry. Unfortunately, resistance has developed in many fungi, especially after fungicides have been used intensively on crops. Farmers of several crops—including potato, soybean, sugar beet, sunflower, and others—have dealt with fungicide failure caused by fungicide resistance (Fig. 35). Resistance can develop over decades of use or within only a few years after initial use. For example, QoI-resistant strains of *Cercospora sojina*, the fungus that causes frogeye leaf spot on soybean (Fig. 36), have been identified in several areas of the United States (Zhang et al., 2012). Resistance was confirmed approximately 4 years after this fungicide class was first used for management of frogeye leaf spot on soybean.

How Fungicide Resistance Develops

Fungicide resistance can occur when a selection pressure is placed on the fungal population. Characteristics of both the fungicide and the pathogen

Fig. 35. Mefenoxam and metalaxyl were once effective and widely used for sunflower downy mildew (infected plant on right), but these chemicals are no longer considered useful because of pathogen resistance. (Courtesy Samuel Markell)

Fig. 36. Strains of *Cercospora sojina*, the fungus that causes frogeye leaf spot on soybean, with resistance to quinone outside inhibitor (QoI) fungicides have been identified in several states. (Courtesy Daren S. Mueller)

determine the magnitude of the selection pressure and the risk of resistance occurring. Fungicides that have a single site of action typically are more at risk for selection of resistance than those that have multi-site activity. Fungal pathogens that regularly undergo sexual reproduction are more likely to have greater variability in the population, which increases the chances of developing a strain that is less sensitive to a fungicide. Additionally, fungal pathogens that have a repeating spore stage (polycyclic pathogens) are more likely to develop resistance to a fungicide, in part because of the high number of spores they produce within a season.

The applicator has control over fungicide-based selection pressure but not the variability of the pathogen. Managing selection pressure is vital to reducing the risk of fungicide resistance.

The Fungicide Resistance Action Committee and the FRAC Code

The Fungicide Resistance Action Committee (FRAC) is an international group that provides guidelines and recommendations to manage the development of fungicide resistance.[1] FRAC developed a code of numbers and letters that can be used to distinguish

___
[1] For more information on the Fungicide Resistance Action Committee (FRAC), go to www.frac.info/frac/index.htm.

different fungicide groups based on their modes of action. The FRAC code can be found on the product label of every fungicide (Fig. 5, page 4). A fungus that becomes resistant to a specific fungicide may be resistant to many or all of the fungicides with the same FRAC code—a condition that is referred to as **cross-resistance**. Table 6 (pages 32–33) provides the FRAC codes for the fungicide groups currently applied to field crops in the United States and Canada.

Management Practices for Fungicide Resistance

Several practices can be applied to minimize the risk that a fungus will become resistant to a fungicide. The best management program for fungicide resistance utilizes all available practices to prolong the life and effectiveness of a fungicide.

Monitoring Programs

One of the first steps in implementing a fungicide resistance management program is to develop baseline levels of sensitivity using laboratory analysis (Fig. 37). The term **baseline level** refers to the amount of the fungicide necessary to effectively control a fungal plant pathogen population that has never been exposed to the fungicide. In other words, the baseline reflects the pathogen population's sensitivity to the fungicide when it is first used.

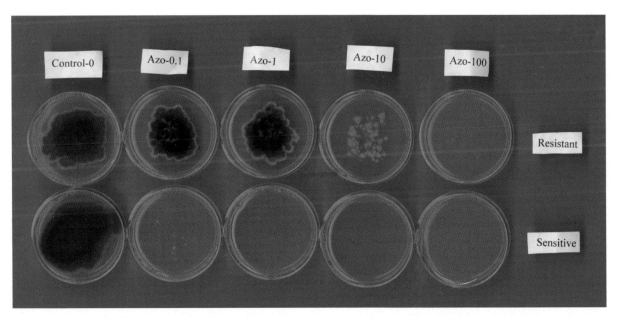

Fig. 37. Evaluating fungicide sensitivity using different concentrations of fungicide. (Courtesy Guirong Zhang)

TABLE 6. Fungicides available for use on different field crops[a]

FRAC Code	Group Name	Active Ingredient Common Name	Risk of Resistance
1	Methyl benzimidazole carbamates (MBC)	Thiabendazole	High
		Thiophanate-methyl	
2	Dicarboximides	Iprodione	Medium to high
		Vinclozolin	
3	Demethylation inhibitors (DMI)[b]	Cyproconazole	Medium
		Difenoconazole	
		Fenbuconazole	
		Flutriafol	
		Imazalil	
		Metconazole	
		Myclobutanil	
		Propiconazole	
		Prothioconazole	
		Tebuconazole	
		Tetraconazole	
		Triticonazole	
4	Phenylamides	Mefenoxam	High
		Metalaxyl	
7	Succinate dehydrogenase inhibitors (SDHI)[c]	Boscalid	Medium
		Carboxin	
		Fluopyram	
		Flutolanil	
		Fluxapyroxad	
		Penthiopyrad	
		Sedaxane	
9	Anilino-pyrimidines (AP)	Cyprodinil	Medium
		Pyrimethanil	
11	Quinone outside inhibitors (QoI)[d]	Azoxystrobin	High
		Famoxadone	
		Fenamidone	
		Fluoxastrobin	
		Picoxystrobin	
		Pyraclostrobin	
		Trifloxystrobin	
12	Phenylpyrroles (PP)	Fludioxonil	Low to medium

[a] Data from Fungicide Resistance Action Committee (2012).
[b] Some fungicides in the DMI group may be referred to as triazoles or imidazoles.
[c] Some fungicides in the SDHI group may be referred to as carboxamides.
[d] Some fungicides in the QoI group may be referred to as strobilurins.

(continued)

TABLE 6. Continued

FRAC Code	Group Name	Active Ingredient Common Name	Risk of Resistance
14	Aromatic hydrocarbons (AH)	Chloroneb	Low to medium
		Quintozene (PCNB)	
21	Quinone inside inhibitors (QiI)	Cyazofamid	Medium to high
22	Benzamides	Zoxamide	Low to medium
27	Cyanoacetamide-oximes	Cymoxanil	Low to medium
28	Carbamates	Propamocarb	Low to medium
29	Oxidative phosphorylation uncouplers	Fluazinam	Low
30	Organo tin compounds	Fentin hydroxide (triphenyltin hydroxide)	Low to medium
32	Heteroaromatics	Hymexazol	Not known
33	Phosphonates	Phosphorous acid and salts	Low
40	Carboxylic acid amides (CAA)	Dimethomorph	Low to medium
		Mandipropamid	
M	Multisite activity	Captan	Low
		Chlorothalonil	
		Copper	
		Mancozeb	
		Maneb	
		Metiram	
		Sulfur	
		Thiram	

Once the baseline level has been established, a monitoring program can be implemented to determine whether the pathogen population is becoming less sensitive to the fungicide over time. Generally, a monitoring program consists of collecting samples of the pathogen and testing them periodically in a laboratory for sensitivity to the fungicide.

After every fungicide application, the field should be scouted to evaluate how well the fungicide has worked and to identify signs of product failure (Fig. 38). Although a fungicide might fail for a variety of reasons (see pages 20–24), it is important to determine if fungicide resistance is a possible factor. Doing so involves contacting the chemical company representative or personnel from local extension services.

Fig. 38. Scouting after applying fungicides will help identify signs of product failure. (Courtesy Marcia McMullen)

IPM Practices

Scouting fields regularly, monitoring the development and movement of diseases regionally, and applying a recommended fungicide when there is a high risk for disease development are all parts of a successful **integrated pest management (IPM)** program. Applying fungicide only when necessary is important for prolonging the effective life span of a product (Fig. 39). Many fungicide products and active ingredients (or similar products with the same mode of action) are registered for use across several field crops—some of which grow in rotation with one another. Applying a fungicide when the economic yield loss from a disease is relatively low can increase the risk of selecting for a fungicide-resistant population.

Conserving the existing fungicide groups is extremely important, because few other groups are effective on the field crop pathogens that currently exist. Using IPM practices will help conserve these products for the management of field crop diseases for years to come.

Fungicide Mixtures and Alternation

Tank mixing fungicides or applying premixed products with different modes of action can help reduce the selection pressure placed on the pathogen population compared with using only a single product. Tank mixing reduces the risk of fungicide resistance, because if a mutant spore develops resistance to one fungicide, it will be killed by the other fungicide in the mix. Tank mixing is effective only if both fungicides control the target pathogen. For example, tank mixing tetraconazole plus thiophanate-methyl would not be a good fungicide resistance management practice for soybean rust, because thiophanate-methyl is not effective against the pathogen that causes this disease.

If more than one fungicide application is required during a season, then fungicides with different modes of action should be used. For example, a QoI fungicide can be applied first, followed by a DMI fungicide later in the crop's development. When alternating fungicides, each fungicide should be applied at the time when it will be most effective on the diseases being managed.

Fig. 39. Applying fungicide only when necessary is important for resistance management. (Courtesy Gary Munkvold)

Label Recommendations

Another important component of fungicide resistance management is following the product label, which is the law. Some fungicides have restrictions on the number of applications that can be made during a season or restrictions on making back-to-back applications.

Following fungicide label rates is not only a key component of disease management but also important to an effective fungicide-resistance program. When sublethal doses of a fungicide are applied, the risk increases that fungal pathogens will become less sensitive to the chemical.

Guidelines for Management of Fungicide Resistance

Management of fungicide resistance is important in the production of all field crops. The risk of fungicide resistance developing can be reduced by following these guidelines:

- If a fungicide is applied, monitor the crop for disease progress. Ineffective control by the fungicide can indicate resistance.
- Tank mix fungicides or use premix products with different modes of action.
- Use good agronomic practices to reduce the need for fungicides.
- Apply a fungicide only when necessary.
- Follow the label. Use recommended rates, and obey restrictions.

Chemical Classes

FRAC Code 1: Methyl Benzimidazole Carbamate (MBC) Fungicides

MBC fungicides are registered on many different field crops as both seed-applied and foliar-applied products. These fungicides are effective against a broad range of fungi that can cause leaf spots, root and crown rots, stem rots, and powdery mildews (Fig. 40), but they are not effective against the fungi that cause rust diseases.

Mode of action: MBC fungicides inhibit tubulin biosynthesis, which interferes with cell shape and normal cell division (mitosis) in sensitive fungi. MBC fungicides have both preventive and early infection activity on target fungi.

Mobility in plants: MBC fungicides have systemic properties, but they cannot move downward in the plant. They are more effective when complete coverage of the plant is achieved.

FRAC Code 2: Dicarboximide Fungicides

Dicarboximide fungicides are used on many different types of plants, including field crops. These fungicides are highly effective against several different fungal pathogens.

Mode of action: Dicarboximide fungicides interfere with the osmotic signal transduction pathway, which affects germination of spores and growth of mycelium.

Mobility in plants: Some dicarboximide fungicides exhibit locally systemic properties.

FRAC Code 3: Demethylation Inhibitor (DMI) Fungicides

DMI fungicides were introduced in the mid-1970s and include the triazoles. They are highly effective against the pathogens of many different fungal diseases, especially powdery mildews, rusts (Fig. 41), and leaf spots.

Fig. 40. Powdery mildew of soybean. (Courtesy Daren S. Mueller)

Fig. 41. Wheat stem rust. (Courtesy Marcia McMullen)

Mode of action: DMI fungicides inhibit one specific enzyme, C14-demethylase, which has a role in sterol production in fungi. One such sterol, ergosterol, is necessary for fungal membrane structure and function and is thus essential for the development of functional cell walls. Therefore, these fungicides cause abnormal fungal growth and eventually death.

Each DMI fungicide may act at a slightly different location in the biochemical sterol-producing pathway. While the results are similar in various fungi (abnormal fungal growth and death), there are great differences in the activity spectra of these fungicides. DMI fungicides have no effect against spore germination, because spores contain enough sterol to initiate the formation of germination tubes. Some spores even have enough sterol to produce infection structures; therefore, in some cases, DMI fungicides may not be effective against initial infection of the host tissue.

DMI fungicides may be applied preventively or early in the fungal infection process. Some have antisporulant properties, which means they inhibit spore production and thus help to slow down disease development. However, once a fungus has begun to produce spores on an infected plant, DMI fungicides are no longer effective against it.

Mobility in plants: Although DMI fungicides do not have the degree of systemic movement that characterizes many herbicides, they are locally systemic and more mobile in plant tissues than QoI fungicides. Following application, the active ingredient is readily taken up by the leaves and moves within them. Studies have shown that three droplets of a DMI fungicide applied at a labeled rate to a soybean trifoliate leaf circulate through the entire leaf within 1 day. It should be noted, however, that DMI fungicides are not necessarily transported from one leaf to another leaf or from one part of the plant to another part. They also do not move downward through the phloem.

FRAC Code 4: Phenylamide Fungicides

Phenylamide fungicides are used to control oomycete pathogens, such as *Pythium* and *Phytophthora* species (Fig. 42). These fungicides are often used as seed treatments or in-furrow treatments.

Mode of action: Phenylamide fungicides inhibit the synthesis of ribonucleic acid (RNA), which affects mycelial growth and the formation of spores and infection structures.

Mobility in plants: Phenylamide fungicides exhibit systemic properties, moving primarily upward.

FRAC Code 7: Succinate Dehydrogenase Inhibitor (SDHI) Fungicides

SDHI fungicides differ in their methods of application and spectrums of diseases controlled. They can be applied to foliage, as seed treatments, or via in-furrow methods.

Mode of action: SDHI fungicides inhibit fungal respiration.

Mobility in plants: These fungicides are locally systemic. Movement of SDHI fungicides is translaminar and upward.

FRAC Code 9: Anilino-Pyrimidine (AP) Fungicides

AP fungicides are applied primarily as foliar treatments and have activity against *Botrytis* species and a few other fungi.

Fig. 42. Soybean seedlings with symptoms of damping-off caused by *Pythium* species. (Courtesy Daren S. Mueller)

Mode of action: AP fungicides inhibit the synthesis of amino acids. This activity inhibits fungal penetration and fungal growth both inside and outside the leaf.

Mobility in plants: These fungicides are systemic and move upward in the plant.

FRAC Code 11: Quinone Outside Inhibitor (QoI) Fungicides

QoI fungicides are very effective on a broad spectrum of fungi and used on most field crops. They include the strobilurins, which were derived from a naturally occurring compound found in wood-rotting fungi. Other QoI fungicides are synthetic.

Mode of action: QoI fungicides act at the quinone outer binding site of the cytochrome bc1 complex (complex II of fungal respiration). In other words, these fungicides act by inhibiting respiration in fungal mitochondria, thereby stopping energy production, which results in the death of the fungus. This group of fungicides should be applied preventively or as early as possible in the disease cycle. They are effective against spore germination and early fungal growth.

Mobility in plants: Most QoI fungicides are locally systemic. They are absorbed into leaf tissue. If a droplet of fungicide is applied to the top surface of a leaf, it will spread out on that surface and move to the other leaf surface by translaminar redistribution. Some of these fungicides move upward in the plant through the xylem. Additionally, some may move as a gas above the leaf and readily rebind to the waxy leaf surface.

FRAC Code 12: Phenylpyrrole (PP) Fungicides

PP fungicides include fludioxonil, which is used primarily as a seed treatment and exhibits a broad spectrum of disease control. Fludioxonil is also used on a limited basis as a foliar fungicide on a few crops.

Mode of action: PP fungicides interfere with the osmotic signal transduction pathway, affecting the germination of spores and growth of mycelia.

Mobility in plants: PP fungicides do not have systemic properties and do not move within the plant.

FRAC Code 14: Aromatic Hydrocarbon (AH) Fungicides

AH fungicides are used primarily as seed treatments on some field crops. Some AH fungicides can be applied as foliar or in-furrow treatments.

Mode of action: The mode of action of AH fungicides is not certain. However, researchers have proposed that these fungicides interfere with lipid and membrane synthesis, which are important for fungal mycelium growth.

Mobility in plants: Some AH fungicides have upward systemic activity; others are redistributed on the plant through the vapor phase.

FRAC Code 21: Quinone Inside Inhibitor (QiI) Fungicides

At present, the only QiI fungicide commercially available is cyazofamid, which has activity against oomycetes. It is labeled for control of late blight on potato (Fig. 43).

Mode of action: QiI fungicides inhibit respiration and energy production by affecting the same enzyme as the QoI fungicides. However, they act at the quinone inside (Qi) binding site. Although QoI and QiI fungicides act on the same enzyme, they are in different FRAC classes because they bind to different sites.

Mobility in plants: Cyazofamid has limited systemic activity.

Fig. 43. Late blight on potato. (Courtesy Amanda J. Gevens)

FRAC Code 22: Benzamide Fungicides

The only benzamide fungicide currently labeled for use on field crops is zoxamide, which specifically targets diseases caused by oomycetes.

Mode of action: Benzamide fungicides destroy microtubule assembly, which affects mitosis and cell division. Both germ tube and fungal mycelium growth are inhibited.

Mobility in plants: Zoxamide is not a systemic fungicide, but it does have some residual efficacy.

FRAC Code 27: Cyanoacetamide-Oxime Fungicides

Currently, the only cyanoacetamide-oxime fungicide available for use on field crops is cymoxanil. This product is applied as a seed treatment to cut-potato seed pieces or as a foliar application to potato plants to control oomycete pathogens.

Mode of action: The mode of action for cymoxanil is unknown, but it is a preventive fungicide with some early infection activity.

Mobility in plants: Cymoxanil has local systemic activity.

FRAC Code 28: Carbamate Fungicides

The only carbamate fungicide available is propamocarb, which is labeled for use against early and late blight of potato. Propamocarb is also available for use on certain vegetables, turfgrasses, and ornamentals, as well as some greenhouse-grown plants.

Mode of action: Carbamate fungicides disrupt the formation of fungal cell walls by interfering with the synthesis of phospholipids and fatty acids. These fungicides also affect fungal mycelium growth, spore production, and germination.

Mobility in plants: Carbamate fungicides are protectant fungicides with systemic activity. They are absorbed by the roots and leaves and transported upward in the plant.

FRAC Code 29: Oxidative Phosphorylation Uncoupler Fungicides

The oxidative phosphorylation uncoupler fungicide currently available for field crops is fluazinam, which is labeled for use against late blight on potato and white mold (Sclerotinia stem rot) on some crops. Fluazinam also has a local-needs registration on potato powdery scab in several northern U.S. potato-producing states.

Mode of action: These fungicides act by inhibiting energy production. Respiration continues (in contrast to the inhibitory effect of the QoI fungicides), but the energy is not converted to a usable form, eventually leading to cell death. Fluazinam inhibits spore germination and the formation of infection structures.

Mobility in plants: Fluazinam is a protectant fungicide and has no systemic activity.

FRAC Code 30: Organo Tin Compound Fungicides

Fentin hydroxide (triphenyltin hydroxide) is the only fungicide in the organo tin compound class that is registered for use on field crops. It is used to control Cercospora leaf blight on sugar beet (Fig. 44) and

Fig. 44. Cercospora leaf blight on sugar beet. (Courtesy Mohamed Khan)

early blight and late blight on potato. Care must be taken when applying this fungicide, because the combination of certain formulations and additives can increase phytotoxicity. Triphenyltin hydroxide is a restricted use fungicide.

Mode of action: The organo tin compound fungicides disrupt oxidative phosphorylation, which inhibits respiration in the target fungus.

Mobility in plants: This group of fungicides is not systemic.

FRAC Code 32: Heteroaromatic Fungicides

Heteroaromatic fungicides are used to control oomycete pathogens. Hymexazol is currently the only fungicide registered for use on field crops in this class. It is used as a seed treatment to control soilborne pathogens on sugar beet.

Mode of action: Hymexazol affects the targeted pathogens by inhibiting nucleic acid synthesis.

Mobility in plants: Hymexazol has upward systemic properties.

FRAC Code 33: Phosphonate Fungicides

Phosphonate compounds are systemic fungicides that manage oomycete diseases such as late blight and pink rot and fungal diseases such as silver scurf of potato (Fig. 45). Disease control resulting from foliar applications has also been noted postharvest in potato tubers. These fungicides are most effective when applied prior to disease development, but they do have some early infection activity and can be applied when plants display the initial symptoms of a disease. Phosphonate fungicides should be applied to actively growing plants.

Mode of action: Phosphonate fungicides inhibit spore germination and block development of fungal mycelium. These fungicides also enhance the plant's own natural defense system against disease.

Mobility in plants: These compounds are rapidly absorbed through the leaves and roots, and translocation occurs both upward and downward inside the plant. Phosphonate compounds are the only fungicides that are fully systemic.

FRAC Code 40: Carboxylic Acid Amide (CAA) Fungicides

CAA fungicides are effective against oomycete pathogens. These fungicides should be applied just before the onset of infection or when the first visible signs of disease occur within or nearby the field.

Mode of action: CAA fungicides affect the formation of cell walls.

Mobility in plants: CAA fungicides are systemic and move up the treated plant stem and into growing leaves. These fungicides also have antisporulant activity, which helps prevent the spread of disease.

FRAC Code M: Multisite Activity Fungicides

Fungicides with multisite activity are applied to the leaf and stem surfaces and are considered protective or preventive fungicides. These fungicides have a broad spectrum of disease control activity. They inhibit fungi on the plant surface, so the pathogen is not able to infect the plant.

Fig. 45. Silver scurf on potato tuber. (Courtesy Amanda J. Gevens)

Mode of action: Fungicides with multisite activity simultaneously attack multiple biochemical sites within the pathogen. They should be applied preventively, as they do not affect fungi once these pathogens have infected the plant.

Mobility in plants: Fungicides with multisite activity remain on the plant surface and do not penetrate the plant. They remain active only as long as the fungicide remains on the plant surface in sufficient concentration to inhibit fungal growth (usually 7–14 days).

Guidelines for Monitoring Residue from Protective Fungicides

On plant surfaces, contact fungicides are sensitive to environmental conditions such as rainfall and solar radiation. They are unlike systemic fungicides, which are absorbed into the leaf after application (once the residue has dried). General guidelines for monitoring the effects of rain on washing off protective fungicides are as follow:

- **Less than 1 inch** of rain since the last spray will not affect the residue significantly.
- **One to 2 inches** of rain since the last spray will reduce the residue by half.
- **More than 2 inches** of rain since the last spray will remove most of the residue.

Part IV
Using Fungicides to Manage Diseases on Field Crops

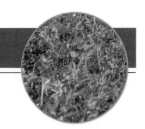

Alfalfa

Many diseases can reduce the health and longevity of alfalfa stands growing in the north-central regions of the United States and Canada. Diseases can also reduce the yield and feed or nutritional value of the crop. Alfalfa diseases can be classified as those affecting the roots, crowns, and stems and those affecting the foliage (leaves) (Fig. 46).

Scouting and proper disease diagnosis are critical for developing the best management tactics. Management is accomplished primarily through the use of resistant cultivars, cultural practices, and fungicides, especially in seed production fields. Fungicides can control many seedling and leaf and stem diseases caused by fungi.

Foliar Fungicides

Leaf and stem diseases pose an ongoing challenge in alfalfa forage production. Although these diseases are influenced by many factors, their development and spread are particularly dependent on environmental conditions and management practices—most notably, harvest in relation to growth stage.

Before deciding to apply a foliar fungicide, the farmer should consider the current weather forecast and its potential effect on disease development. For example, if weather conditions are unfavorable for disease development (dry and hot) or if foliar disease symptoms are not observed as the crop approaches the time of forage harvest, then a fungicide application may not be warranted or economical. Different criteria are used for alfalfa seed production. Farmers should take into account the preharvest interval (PHI), which is usually 14 days. They should also check fungicide labels for the number of applications allowed per harvest period or per year.

Other management practices that may limit alfalfa foliar disease development include the following:

- planting a winter-hardy, disease-resistant cultivar
- rotating with nonhost crops
- harvesting under favorable conditions and at growth stages conducive for optimal forage feed value
- maintaining optimal soil fertility
- avoiding mechanical injury caused by equipment traffic
- preventing animals from overgrazing

Fig. 46. Rust (left) and common leaf spot (right) are two foliar diseases of alfalfa. (Courtesy Samuel Markell [left] and Craig Grau [right])

Seed Treatments

Most alfalfa seed has a fungicide seed treatment to protect from losses caused by Phytophthora and Pythium damping-off in new plantings. Seed treatments will not protect against soilborne pathogens that attack plants beyond the establishment stage.

Other practices for seedling disease management include the following:

- selecting cultivars resistant to *Phytophthora* and *Aphanomyces* species
- improving drainage of fields with slow-draining soils
- correcting soil fertility and pH for optimal alfalfa growth
- preparing a firm, weed-free seedbed for uniform establishment

TABLE 7. Alfalfa diseases and their responses to fungicides

Disease(s)	Causal Agent(s)	Comments
Anthracnose crown and stem rot	*Colletotrichum trifolii*	This disease is favored by hot, moist weather and affects both plant stems and crowns. Foliar fungicides are registered for stem infection, but seed treatments and foliar fungicides are not effective against crown infection.
Aphanomyces root rot	*Aphanomyces euteiches*	The fungus survives on infected plants or crop residue and prefers heavy, saturated soils. It can cause symptoms on both seedlings and older plants, but risk declines with the age of the stand. Regrowth of infected plants is slow following harvest and winter. Fungicide seed treatments for *Pythium* and *Phytophthora* species are not effective against *A. euteiches*.
Bacterial wilt	*Clavibacter michiganensis* subsp. *insidiosus* (*Corynebacterium insidiosum*)	Symptoms affect roots, leaves, and overall vigor and are most noticeable in regrowth after cutting. Fungicides are not labeled and should not be used for management.
Brown root rot	*Phoma sclerotioides*	The causal agent infects dormant alfalfa during the winter and thrives when the soil temperature is less than 60°F (16°C). It is therefore most active in the fall and spring, when plants are dormant and environmental conditions are favorable for infection. Fungicide seed treatments are not effective against brown root rot.
Common leaf spot	*Pseudopeziza medicaginis*	Leaves develop small, brown spots, which form disklike centers and become raised as they age. Fungicides are most effective if applied at the first sign of disease or at the beginning of flowering.
Crown and root rot complex	*Fusarium* spp., *Rhizoctonia solani*, *Phoma* spp.	These fungi can infect plants alone or in combination, and symptoms can be found in most fields. The most typical symptom is darkening (rot) of the crown. Symptoms increase over time and can substantially reduce stand longevity, especially under stressful conditions. Fungicide seed treatments are not effective.
Downy mildew	*Peronospora trifoliorum*	This disease is common but rarely causes severe damage. Spots develop on upper leaf surfaces, and a fungus grows on lower leaf surfaces. Cool, wet (rainy) weather favors development of the disease. Foliar fungicides are effective, but applying them is often not economical unless the crop is intended for seed production.
Environmental conditions	Drought, frost damage, nutrient deficiencies, and so on	Symptoms of environmental damage can be confused with those of alfalfa diseases. For treatment to be effective, it must be determined whether disease or environmental conditions are responsible for the problems observed in the field.
Fusarium wilt	*Fusarium oxysporum* f. sp. *medicaginis*	Fusarium wilt is often confused with bacterial wilt, but the former causes roots to have a characteristic brown discoloration. Seed treatment fungicides are not effective.

(continued)

TABLE 7. Continued

Disease(s)	Causal Agent(s)	Comments
Leptosphaerulina (Lepto) leaf spot	*Leptosphaerulina briosiani*	Lepto leaf spot can be confused with common leaf spot. Symptoms of the former begin as small, black spots with tan or brown centers and yellow haloes; as the spots grow, they join to form larger lesions. Foliar fungicides are effective but not often economical unless the crop is intended for seed production.
Nematode diseases	Several	General symptoms include yellowing and stunting of plants and are often observed in patches in the field. Diagnosis involves examining roots for signs of nematodes or collecting soil for lab analysis. Fields with nematode damage often have a higher incidence of crown and root rot, as well. Fungicides are not labeled for management and should not be used for these diseases.
Phytophthora root rot	*Phytophthora medicaginis*	*P. medicaginis* is an important soilborne pathogen of alfalfa (Fig. 47). Infection often occurs as seedlings emerge, but mature plants may be infected and express symptoms. Disease development is favored by cool and water-saturated soils. Fungicide seed treatments containing metalaxyl or mefenoxam are available but prevent infection only during seed germination and for a short period of time after seedling emergence.
Pythium seed rot, damping-off, and seedling blight	*Pythium* spp.	These are predominantly early season diseases. Infection often occurs from the time of planting to several weeks after the emergence of seedlings. Disease development is favored by cool, wet soils. Fungicide seed treatments containing metalaxyl or mefenoxam are available but prevent loss only during seed germination and for a short period of time after emergence.

Fig. 47. Phytophthora root rot on alfalfa. (Courtesy Craig Grau)

(continued)

TABLE 7. Continued

Disease(s)	Causal Agent(s)	Comments
Rust	*Uromyces striatus*	Reddish-brown spore masses are produced on the upper surfaces of leaves, petioles, and stems. Foliar fungicides should be applied when alfalfa is in the early flowering stage.
Sclerotinia crown and stem rot	*Sclerotinia trifoliorum, S. sclerotiorum*	Symptoms begin as small, brown spots on leaves and stems, followed by expanded, white stem lesions and wilt. Symptoms of crown rot follow, including the darkening (rot) of crown tissues and the growth of white mycelia and black sclerotia. Disease is favored by cool, wet (humid) weather, and plants less than 1 year old are most susceptible. Alfalfa crops seeded in late summer and fall are particularly prone to developing the disease. Fungicides are available for use, but application timing is critical. Application should be made during the crop's early flowering stage (20–50% bloom), since fungicides are ineffective beyond this stage.
Spring black stem and leaf spot	*Phoma medicaginis*	Small, dark spots ("tar" spots) with irregular borders develop on the leaves, petioles, and lower stem and then move up the plant canopy. Disease development is favored by extended periods of wet, cool weather. Foliar fungicides are available for use.
Stemphylium leaf spot	*Stemphylium botryosum*	Light-tan lesions form on upper leaves. Disease is favored by cool, wet weather. Foliar fungicides are effective but not often economical unless the crop is intended for seed production.
Verticillium wilt	*Verticillium albo-atrum*	Verticillium wilt is most common in stands at least 2 years old. Leaves on the upper stems become distorted and turn light green to tannish pink. Fungicides are not effective.
Viruses	Several	Several viruses can cause diseases in alfalfa (such as alfalfa mosaic), and the symptoms may be confused with those of fungal diseases. Virus diseases differ by region. Fungicides are not labeled for management and should not be used for these diseases.
Winter crown rot (snow mold)	*Microdochium nivale, Typhula* spp.	The characteristic symptom is a dark-brown rot of the crown, which is often observed after a winter during which heavy snow falls early in the season. This snowfall insulates the ground from freezing, allowing fungi to grow and infect plants. Fungicides are not effective for treating snow mold.

Canola

Foliar Fungicides

Foliar fungicides are important management tools for blackleg and Sclerotinia stem rot of canola:

- **Blackleg:** Fungicide applications may reduce early infections and lessen yield reductions that result from this disease. An application made during the two- to four-leaf stage is most effective in protecting against blackleg (Fig. 48).

- **Sclerotinia stem rot:** Environmental conditions favoring Sclerotinia stem rot (also called white mold) include ample soil moisture prior to bloom (a minimum of 1–2 inches [2.5–5.0 cm] of rain 1–2 weeks before bloom is needed for inoculum production), moderate temperatures (approximately 60–75°F [16–24°C]), and a wet canopy during bloom. When conditions are favorable, fungicides applied in the early bloom growth stages can reduce disease and yield loss from this disease. Depending on the growing region, numerous decision-making aids may be available, which include disease-forecasting or -risk models and rubric-style risk checklists.

Seed Treatments

Several pathogens can cause seedling diseases, and most seed is sold pretreated. Broad-spectrum seed treatments provide some management of fungi (*Fusarium* and *Rhizoctonia* species) and oomycetes (*Pythium* species). Fungicide seed treatments can reduce blackleg when seed is infected; however, infection from seed is not considered very important in the United States. Production of pathogen-free seed is the best management strategy.

Fig. 48. Symptoms of blackleg on canola, including stem lesions (top and middle) and leaf lesions (bottom). (Courtesy Samuel Markell [top and middle] and Carl A. Bradley [bottom])

TABLE 8. Canola diseases and their responses to fungicides

Disease(s)	Causal Agent(s)	Comments
Alternaria diseases (leaf spot, pod spot, black spot)	*Alternaria brassicae, A. brassicicola*	These diseases are common in North America but generally do not cause economic loss. Although the use of fungicides may reduce incidence of the diseases, it may not be economically viable.
Aster yellows	Phytoplasma	Yellows is found sporadically in U.S. production. Symptoms include bladder-shaped pods and discoloration of tissue. The causal agent is a bacterium in the class Mollicutes. Fungicides are neither labeled nor effective and should not be used for management.
Blackleg (Phoma stem canker)	*Leptosphaeria maculans* (teleomorph *Phoma lingam*), *L. biglobosa*	This disease is widespread in North America, and yield loss can occur when infection develops during a crop's early vegetative stages. Fungicide seed treatments may reduce disease resulting from infected seeds, whereas application of foliar fungicides in the early vegetative growth stages may reduce infections caused by airborne inoculum.
Clubroot	*Plasmodiophora brassicae*	Clubroot has not yet been found in the United States, but it occurs in Canada. It causes damage to the roots, which reduces yield, and is most common in acidic soils. Fungicides are not recommended for control of this disease.
Downy mildew	*Hyaloperonospora parasitica*	This disease occurs infrequently in North America and is generally not considered a threat to yield or quality. Symptoms appear as discolored lesions on the leaf's upper surface and white sporulation on the leaf's under surface. Although fungicides may be effective, they typically are not economically viable.
Nematode diseases	Several	Several nematodes can cause diseases in canola, but the causal agents differ by region. Fungicides are not labeled for management and should not be used for these diseases.
Root rots and seedling diseases	*Fusarium* spp., *Rhizoctonia* spp., others	Root rots and seedling diseases on canola may be economically important. Fungicide seed treatments may offer some protection; thus, most commercial seed is sold pretreated.
Sclerotinia stem rot (white mold)	*Sclerotinia sclerotiorum*	This disease is widespread and frequently causes yield loss when weather is favorable (moist soil and moderate temperatures) (Fig. 49). Fungicides applied at the early to midbloom stages can reduce disease and yield loss.
Viruses	Several	Several viruses can cause diseases in canola, and the symptoms may be confused with those of fungal diseases. Virus diseases differ by region. Fungicides are not labeled for management and should not be used for these diseases.
White rust (staghead)	*Albugo candida*	Symptoms include white pustules on aboveground plant parts. Foliar fungicides are effective for management. However, the disease has not been reported in major production areas of the United States, so the economics of fungicide application are uncertain.

Fig. 49. Sclerotia of Sclerotinia stem rot on canola. (Courtesy Samuel Markell)

Corn

Foliar Fungicides

Foliar fungal diseases of corn are managed with a combination of resistant hybrids, crop rotation, tillage, and foliar fungicides. Use of foliar fungicides has increased in recent years (Wise and Mueller, 2011), in part because marketing materials have touted a variety of claims for these products, including yield benefits in the absence of disease. Regardless, the most important benefit that foliar fungicides provide is disease management (Fig. 50).

University fungicide trials indicate that the presence of disease plays an important role in consistently achieving economically positive yield responses with or without foliar fungicides (Table 5, page 20) (Wise and Mueller, 2011). The challenge lies in predicting before or at tasseling what disease levels will be several weeks later.

To help predict the need for applying a foliar fungicide on corn, farmers should consider these factors:

- Specialty corn (such as inbreds, sweet corn, and popcorn) may have different economic and other considerations than field corn hybrids (Fig. 51). Hybrids also vary in their susceptibility to foliar diseases. Seed companies typically can provide information on the susceptibility of their hybrids to common diseases, such as gray leaf spot and northern leaf blight. In general, the hybrids that are the most susceptible to fungal foliar diseases should be the targets of fungicide applications if the risk for disease is relatively high.

- Cropping history and percentage of surface crop residue affect the risk of disease development. Many pathogens survive in crop residue, which means the risk of foliar diseases increases when corn is planted in the same field in subsequent years.

- Foliar disease development is favored by cloudy, rainy, humid weather. In growing seasons when these conditions are common, the risk for disease development increases.

- Fields with a history of severe foliar disease are likely to develop disease in subsequent years. In addition, field topography can affect disease development. Cool, moist air may pool in low areas of a field, creating extended dew periods. Similarly, in areas of a field surrounded by trees, plant leaves may remain wet for longer periods of time following irrigation, dew, or rain.

Fig. 50. Gray leaf spot is the most common foliar disease on corn in the United States. (Courtesy Daren S. Mueller)

Fig. 51. Most hybrids have adequate levels of resistance to common rust, but fungicides may be needed in specialty corn or crops grown in the southern United States. (Courtesy Gary Munkvold)

Disease levels should be determined by scouting for foliar diseases in corn just before tassel emergence. Key criteria in deciding whether to spray include the following:

- Disease is present on the ear leaf or the three leaves below it.
- A susceptible hybrid has been used.
- The previous crop planted in the field was corn.
- Reduced-till or no-till farming is used in the field.
- Current and future weather conditions favor disease development.

If all five criteria are met, applying a foliar fungicide may be necessary to manage disease. If only a few of the criteria are met, the plants that were observed in the field should be documented and reexamined for disease development within 1 week.

Both weather factors and the crop's growth stage should be considered to determine the need for a fungicide application. Disease presence before or at tasseling may result in greater yield loss than disease that develops during grain fill.

Spraying before tasseling often is not needed in northern production areas. This recommendation will vary from region to region, however, and depends on both the climate early in the season and the corn type. Most foliar fungicides are applied between the stages of tassel emergence and brown silk growth. Use of an adjuvant in fungicide applications prior to tasseling may result in abnormal ear development (Fig. 30, page 24).

The profitability of a fungicide application depends on the yield potential, the price of grain, and the cost of application.

Seed Treatments

Except in organic production, most field corn is treated with a fungicide seed treatment. Commercially available seed treatments contain one or two active ingredients that are effective against fungi (such as *Fusarium* and *Rhizoctonia* species) and oomycetes (such as *Pythium* species) (Fig. 52).

Fig. 52. Rhizoctonia root rot on corn. (Courtesy Alison Robertson)

TABLE 9. Corn diseases and their responses to fungicides		
Disease(s)	**Causal Agent(s)**	**Comments**
Anthracnose leaf blight	*Colletotrichum graminicola*	This early season disease is common in the U.S. Midwest. The fungus survives in crop residue. Fungicides are available for use, but their application does not usually correlate to yield response.
Common rust	*Puccinia sorghi*	Most hybrids have adequate levels of resistance for management, but fungicides may be needed for specialty corn or in southern environments. The fungus does not survive in crop residue.
Common smut	*Ustilago maydis*	This disease is commonly observed but typically not of economic importance. Fungicides are not labeled for smut.
Crazy top	*Sclerophthora macrospora*	Crazy top is observed in fields with early season ponding and excess moisture. Fungicides are not labeled or necessary for this disease.

(continued)

TABLE 9. Continued

Disease(s)	Causal Agent(s)	Comments
Ear rots	*Aspergillus* spp., *Fusarium* spp., *Gibberella zeae, Stenocarpella maydis, Trichoderma viride,* others	Several fungi can cause ear rots. Fungicides may be available for use against particular causal agents but vary in effectiveness.
Eyespot	*Aureobasidium zeae*	Eyespot is a cool-season disease and is most common in northern areas (Fig. 53). Fungicides are available for use and may be necessary for management.
Goss's wilt	*Clavibacter michiganensis* subsp. *nebraskensis*	This bacterial disease can be confused with several foliar fungal diseases (Fig. 54). Fungicides are not labeled and should not be used for management.
Gray leaf spot	*Cercospora zeae-maydis*	Gray leaf spot is the most common foliar disease on corn in the United States. The fungus survives in crop residue. Fungicides are available for use and may be necessary for management.
Head smut	*Sphacelotheca reiliana*	This disease is most common in western production areas. Fungicides are not available for use.
Holcus leaf spot	*Pseudomonas syringae*	This bacterial disease can be confused with eyespot and other foliar fungal diseases. Fungicides are not labeled and should not be used.
Nematode diseases	Several	Several nematodes can cause diseases in corn, but the causal agents differ by region. Fungicides are not labeled for management and should not be used for these diseases.
Northern leaf blight	*Exserohilum turcicum*	Northern leaf blight is a common foliar disease in the U.S. Midwest and Great Plains. The fungus survives in crop residue. Fungicides are available for use and may be necessary for management.
Northern leaf spot (Carbonum leaf spot)	*Bipolaris zeicola*	This disease is most common in northern production regions. The fungus survives in crop residue. Fungicides are labeled for use but may not be necessary for management.

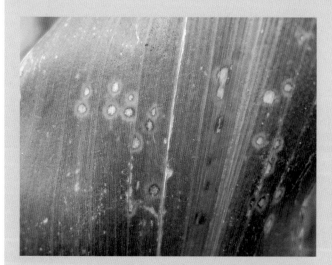

Fig. 53. Eyespot on corn. (Courtesy Alison Robertson)

Fig. 54. Goss's wilt on corn is a bacterial disease that can be confused with northern leaf blight. (Courtesy Casey Schleicher)

(continued)

TABLE 9. Continued

Disease(s)	Causal Agent(s)	Comments
Physoderma brown spot	*Physoderma maydis*	Brown spot is observed sporadically in commercial production. It appears early in the growing season when rains are frequent and can be confused with southern rust and eyespot. Selected fungicides are available for use.
Seed rots, root rots, and seedling blights	*Fusarium* spp., *Rhizoctonia* spp., *Pythium* spp., others	Many fungi can cause seed and root rots, along with seedling blight and stand issues. Seed treatments are applied to manage both seedborne and soilborne pathogens.
Southern leaf blight	*Bipolaris maydis*	Southern leaf blight is observed infrequently and may be confused with other common foliar leaf blights. The fungus survives in crop residue. Fungicides are labeled for use but may not be necessary for management.
Southern rust	*Puccinia polysora*	This is a common foliar disease in the southern United States; in some years, it moves north and can affect states in the Midwest and Great Plains. The fungicide does not survive in corn residue. More than one fungicide application may be needed for management in southern areas.
Stalk rots	*Colletotrichum graminicola*, *Fusarium* spp., *Macrophomina phaseolina*, *Stenocarpella maydis*, others	Several fungi can cause stalk rots; however, stress and other production factors can influence the severity of the rots. Foliar fungicides may reduce stalk rots indirectly by reducing leaf damage from foliar diseases; seed treatments have no effect.
Stewart's disease	*Pantoea stewartii*	This bacterial disease can be confused with fungal leaf blights. Fungicides are not labeled and should not be used.
Viruses	Several	Viruses can cause diseases in corn, and the symptoms may be confused with those of some foliar diseases. Virus diseases differ by region. Fungicides are not labeled for management and should not be used for these diseases.

Cotton

Foliar Fungicides

Currently, the use of foliar fungicides on cotton provides significant yield production from two diseases: southwestern cotton rust and Corynespora leaf spot (Fig. 55). The full importance of Corynespora leaf spot and its true impact on yield remain to be determined. However, this disease seems most severe (and perhaps the use of fungicides most justified) in areas of the southern United States where these conditions are met:

- Cotton is grown in short rotations.
- Corynespora leaf spot has been a problem in the past.
- The disease is observed to be developing in the lower canopy of the crop.
- The foliar canopy is dense and the yield potential is high.

Fungicides may also be an effective management tool for Ascochyta blight, areolate mildew, and other foliar diseases, but losses from these diseases generally do not warrant fungicide application. Use of fungicides for management of boll rots is not recommended, as products do not easily reach bolls (Fig. 56).

In-Furrow Fungicides and Hopper-Box Treatments

In-furrow fungicides can be used to supplement seed treatments. In-furrow fungicides that offer a zone of protection in the soil around the seed are generally thought to provide better protection than additional fungicide seed treatments. Hopper-box treatments, while effective and convenient, are generally considered less effective than in-furrow fungicides because of the difficulty in ensuring adequate distribution of fungicide within the hopper-box and around the seed. In-furrow and hopper-box fungicide treatments should be considered when planting during periods in which conditions favor disease development.

Seed Treatments

Fungicide seed treatments are a critical tool for the management of cotton seedling diseases (Fig. 57). Seed treatments typically include a combination

Fig. 55. Corynespora leaf spot on cotton. (Courtesy Robert C. Kemerait Jr.)

Fig. 56. Cotton boll rot. (Courtesy Tom Allen)

of fungicides to effectively control the complex of pathogens that can cause seed and seedling diseases. All commercial seed is treated with what is referred to as a **base fungicide treatment**, which is effective in protecting the seed and seedling from disease. It is estimated that in 4 out of 5 years, the base seed treatment is sufficient for disease control. However, additional seed treatments are now available that further reduce the risk of a poor plant stand. Such additional seed treatments are most beneficial for farmers who plant low-vigor seed, plant in cool and wet soils, plant into conservation tillage, plant into fields where short rotations between cotton are practiced, and reduce seeding rates to save on seed cost.

Fig. 57. Rhizoctonia seedling disease on cotton. (Courtesy Robert C. Kemerait Jr.)

TABLE 10. Cotton diseases and their responses to fungicides

Disease(s)	Causal Agent(s)	Comments
Alternaria leaf spot	*Alternaria macrospora, A. alternata*	This disease is associated with nutrient deficiencies (often potassium) caused by insufficient fertilization or drought that reduces uptake by the plant. Fungicides have not been effective in management.
Areolate (false) mildew	*Ramularia gossypii*	So-called false mildew is observed infrequently in the southeastern United States, especially during periods of abundant rainfall and in cotton with rank growth. This disease responds to fungicides, but it is unclear how much yield loss is associated with it.
Ascochyta blight	*Ascochyta gossypii*	Once referred to as wet weather blight, this disease is occasionally problematic, especially when periods of abundant rainfall occur early in the season. Although some fungicides are labeled for management of the disease, they typically are not needed.
Boll rots	Several	Boll rots are caused by a number of different fungi and can lead to severe losses. The use of fungicides to minimize the impact of boll rots has been largely unsuccessful, likely because of the difficulty in getting sufficient fungicide to the bolls through the thick canopy of foliage.
Cercospora leaf spot	*Cercospora gossypina*	Cercospora leaf spot is associated with nutrient deficiencies and is often seen with Stemphylium leaf spot. Fungicides are not believed to be effective in the management of this disease.
Charcoal rot	*Macrophomina phaseolina*	This disease is characterized by severe wilt and plant death in localized areas of a field and is usually observed during periods of drought stress. Charcoal rot does not respond to fungicides.
Corynespora leaf spot	*Corynespora cassiicola*	Severe outbreaks of Corynespora leaf spot are typically associated with rank-growth cotton and abundant rainfall and irrigation. Well-timed fungicide applications improve yields when this is the primary foliar disease in a field. Research continues to determine when fungicides are best used to manage this disease.
Fusarium wilt	*Fusarium oxysporum* f. sp. *vasinfectum*	Fusarium wilt is found in association with plant-pathogenic nematodes. Fungicides are not effective in its management.

(continued)

TABLE 10. Continued

Disease(s)	Causal Agent(s)	Comments
Nematode diseases	Several	Several nematodes can cause diseases in cotton, but the causal agents differ by region. Fungicides are not labeled for management and should not be used for these diseases.
Phymatotrichum root rot	*Phymatotrichopsis omnivora*	This disease kills plants rapidly, and the leaves remain attached to infected plants. Fungicides are not effective in managing this disease.
Seedling diseases	*Pythium* spp., *Rhizoctonia solani*, *Thielaviopsis basicola*, *Fusarium* spp.	Seedling diseases are typically more severe in cool soils, where germination is slowed and vigor is reduced. Commercial seed is treated with a combination of fungicides to protect against seedling diseases.
Southwestern cotton rust	*Puccinia cacabata*	This disease is an occasional problem in upland and pima cotton crops in the U.S. Southwest. Fungicides can reduce losses when the disease is severe. The choice of fungicide and frequency of application depend on prevailing environmental conditions.
Stemphylium leaf spot	*Stemphylium solani*	This disease is associated with nutrient deficiencies (often potassium) caused by insufficient fertilization or drought that reduces uptake by the plant. Fungicides are not effective in management of this disease.
Verticillium wilt	*Verticillium dahliae*	This soilborne fungus causes the leaves to wilt and turn yellow between the veins, and the leaf tissue eventually dies. Plants often have vascular discoloration and may defoliate and die prematurely. Fungicides are not effective against this disease.
Viruses	Several	Several viruses can cause diseases in cotton, and the symptoms may be confused with those of fungal diseases. Virus diseases differ by region. Fungicides are not labeled for management and should not be used for these diseases.

Dry Beans

Foliar Fungicides

Several foliar diseases on dry beans are commonly managed using timely fungicide applications combined with genetic resistance, cultural practices, and disease forecasting. However, the numerous root rot diseases that affect dry beans are generally not treated with foliar fungicides because of the high cost versus the perceived benefit and the impracticality of reaching these soilborne pathogens with spray applications.

Scouting is critical in the management of numerous dry bean diseases. Knowing when to begin looking for certain diseases can be useful in stopping disease in the early stages. White mold (Fig. 58) and rust (Fig. 59) are both late-season diseases and favored by high plant populations and dense canopies combined with cool, humid conditions. The best management of white mold with foliar fungicides can be achieved by one or more timely applications during flowering, before disease symptoms develop. For rust, if infection occurs within 21 days of undercutting (knifing), then yields will seldom be affected and fungicide applications will not be necessary.

A combination of management practices—including fungicide applications and irrigation management—will help control both diseases. For irrigation management, excessive irrigation should be avoided during flowering, because maintaining a low moisture level within the canopy helps reduce the potential for disease development. A crop with a high level of rust needs twice the irrigation as a healthy crop to reach maturity, so adding irrigations will help extend a crop to harvest. Infrequent, heavy watering is preferable to frequent, light watering.

Several important diseases are enhanced following storms with driving winds and hail, including residue-borne bacterial diseases and some fungal leaf spots. Storm events should therefore be considered in deciding whether to apply fungicides or bactericides (copper-containing products).

Making the correct diagnosis is important when scouting for diseases of beans. The ability to distinguish between various diseases is critical for choosing the correct management techniques. For example, confusing bacterial diseases (wilt) with wilting symptoms caused by white mold can result in the unnecessary and ineffective application of a fungicide. Copper is the only foliar chemical treatment available for bacterial diseases. Ozone damage (bronzing) and sunscald of pods and leaves are also commonly confused with rust, which can result in unneeded fungicide application.

Fig. 58. White mold on dry bean. (Courtesy Samuel Markell)

Fig. 59. Rust on dry bean. (Courtesy Samuel Markell)

Seed Treatments

The standard for treating seed includes using several fungicides with different modes of action. The goal is to manage *Pythium* and *Rhizoctonia* species and to delay infection by *Fusarium* species (Fig. 60), which are commonly occurring pathogens of seedlings. Dry bean seed is also treated with an antibiotic to reduce the numerous bacterial pathogens that may be present on the seed or in the field.

Fig. 60. Dry bean stand reductions caused by Pythium root rot (left) and Rhizoctonia root rot on dry bean (right). (Courtesy Robert Harveson)

TABLE 11. Dry bean diseases and their responses to fungicides

Disease(s)	Causal Agent(s)	Comments
Alternaria leaf spot	*Alternaria alternata, A. brassicae, A. brassicicola*	This disease affects all aerial plant parts, but older leaves and mature pods are highly susceptible. Economic loss results from lower prices for discolored seeds. Some fungicides are effective in management, but regulating the moisture content of seed is critical (as excess moisture promotes fungal disease development). The crop should be harvested promptly when dry.
Angular leaf spot	*Phaeoisariopsis griseola*	Angular leaf spot can be confused with nematode angular leaf spot. Planting infected seed into fields with infested residue increases the risk of disease, and moderate temperatures (less than 82°F [28°C]) are conducive for disease development. Seed treatments may be beneficial. Foliar fungicides can prevent or reduce infection if applied early in an epidemic.
Anthracnose	*Colletotrichum lindemuthianum*	This disease, which affects all aboveground plant parts (Fig. 61), has worldwide distribution but is more severe in temperate areas. Fungicides have limited effectiveness because of pathogen variability. Fungicide application should be made at flowering and pod fill if conditions are favorable (cool and wet) for disease development.
Aphanomyces root rot	*Aphanomyces euteiches*	This causal agent is not controlled by metalaxyl, which is effective against other oomycetes (such as *Pythium* species). Crop rotation and the use of resistant cultivars are the primary methods of disease control.
Ashy stem blight	*Macrophomina phaseolina*	Ashy stem blight is an economically important disease in moderate- to high-temperature production areas, particularly in dry conditions. The causal agent contaminates seed and overwinters in residue or soil as small, black sclerotia. Seed treatments are effective for control.

(continued)

TABLE 11. Continued

Disease(s)	Causal Agent(s)	Comments
Bacterial wilt	*Curtobacterium flaccumfaciens* pv. *flaccumfaciens*	Symptoms of bacterial wilt (leaf necrosis and yellowing) may be confused with those of common bacterial blight. Bacterial wilt is favored by temperatures exceeding 90°F (32°C). Fungicides are not effective against this disease, and bactericides have not been tested for effectiveness.
Brown spot	*Pseudomonas syringae* pv. *syringae*	This bacterial disease is favored by moderate temperatures (80–85°F [27–29°C]). Bactericides may be effective if applied before the disease becomes widespread. Fungicides are not labeled and should not be used for management.
Common bacterial blight	*Xanthomonas axonopodis* pv. *phaseoli*	The foliar symptoms of this disease may be confused with those of bacterial wilt. Infected seed and infested residue are common sources of inoculum. Bacterial blight is favored by moderate to high temperatures (85–90°F [27–29°C]). Fungicides are not labeled and should not be used, but bactericides may be effective if applied before the disease becomes widespread.
Fusarium root rot	*Fusarium solani* f. sp. *phaseoli*	Fusarium root rot is extremely common and widely distributed. The causal agent is soilborne; thus, seed treatments may delay but not prevent infection. Plants grown under stressful conditions are more susceptible, and reducing soil compaction may be beneficial in managing the disease.
Fusarium yellows (wilt)	*Fusarium oxysporum* f. sp. *phaseoli*	This *Fusarium* pathogen is soilborne, and like the pathogen of Fusarium root rot, it can survive in the soil for long periods. Fungicide seed treatment may delay infection, and reducing soil compaction may be beneficial.
Gray mold	*Botrytis cinerea*	Gray mold is more serious in snap beans than other bean classes. Disease development is favored by cool, humid conditions, and initial inoculum originates from overwintering sclerotia in the soil. Fungicides are available, but their use is rarely considered economical. If fungicides are used, applications should begin at and continue through flowering.
Halo blight	*Pseudomonas syringae* pv. *phaseolicola*	This disease is favored by low to moderate temperatures (70–75°F [21–24°C]). Infected seed and infested residue are sources of inoculum. Fungicides are not labeled and should not be used, but bactericides may be effective if applied before the disease becomes widespread.

Fig. 61. Anthracnose on dry bean. (Courtesy Samuel Markell)

(continued)

TABLE 11. Continued

Disease(s)	Causal Agent(s)	Comments
Nematode angular leaf spot	Foliar nematode (*Aphelenchoides ritzemabosi*)	The lesions that are characteristic of this disease may appear similar to those of angular leaf spot. Infection is enhanced by free moisture, which allows the nematode to swim on the leaf surface. Epidemics of economic consequence are rare. Alfalfa is a reported alternative host.
Nematode diseases	Several	Several nematodes can causes diseases in dry beans, but the causal agents differ by region. The feeding damage caused by nematodes may produce wilting and foliar symptoms that can be confused with those of other diseases. Fungicides are not effective and should not be used.
Pythium diseases	*Pythium ultimum, P. irregulare, P. aphanidermatum, P. myriotylum*	*Pythium* species are soilborne and can cause seed rots and damping-off, as well as stem and root rot, foliar blight, and pod rots. *P. ultimum* and *P. irregulare* are problematic at low temperatures (below 75°F [24°C]), whereas *P. aphanidermatum* and *P. myriotylum* are problematic at high temperatures (above 90°F [32°C]) and cause root and stem rots late in the season (as soil temperatures rise). The use of seed treatments is standard for reducing emergence problems caused by these pathogens. Foliar fungicides can be used to treat the blight phases of the diseases.
Rhizoctonia root rot	*Rhizoctonia solani*	This common disease occurs most often early in the season, when soil temperatures are low. The causal agent can also induce seedling disease. Fungicides can be effective if applied as seed treatments or soil drenches on young plants.
Rust	*Uromyces appendiculatus*	Rust occurs worldwide but is most common in humid, tropical climates. It can also occur in arid, temperate climates when supplemental irrigation is used. Yield loss can approach 100%; the level of severity depends on the time of infection (with the most severe damage resulting from early infection). Host resistance is the most effective control strategy, but fungicides can also be beneficial if applied at the first signs of infection.
Stem rot	Sterile white basidiomycete (SWB)	This fungus has an extended host range, but it is observed most frequently on snap bean and cowpea planted after corn in irrigated, multiple-cropping systems. The disease is likely of minor importance, but it has been reported to cause hypocotyl lesions of young dry bean in Nebraska.
Viruses	Several	Several viruses can cause diseases in dry beans, but the viruses vary by region. Symptoms of virus diseases may be confused with fertility issues or other abiotic disease problems. Some viruses are favored by the presence of aphid vectors, infected perennial legumes or weeds, and seedborne virus particles. Fungicides are not effective for the control of viruses.
White leaf spot	*Cercospora albida*	This disease is common in several Latin American countries but has also been reported in Minnesota. The causal agent survives in residue from previously infected plants. Some cultivars are resistant to this disease, but the effectiveness of fungicide treatments is unknown.
White mold	*Sclerotinia sclerotiorum*	White mold can cause significant yield loss, especially during cool, wet seasons. Foliar fungicides can effectively manage the disease or at least reduce its severity, but the timing of application is critical. If fungicides are to be applied only once, application should wait until the plants are flowering. If multiple applications are planned, the first application should occur when the plants first start flowering.

Flax

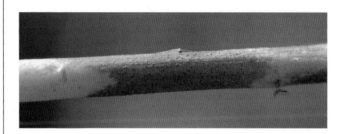

Foliar Fungicides

Fungicides can be used to manage flax seedling diseases, such as Fusarium wilt and various seedling blights, as well as flax foliar diseases, such as pasmo (Fig. 62) and powdery mildew. However, most of these fungicides are in the experimental stage of development and not yet registered for use. There are currently few registered fungicides for flax, and timing the application of these products is critical for controlling fungal disease.

Fungicides currently labeled for use in the United States are effective at reducing pasmo and protecting yield against this disease. These fungicides should be applied at midbloom, although their effectiveness can vary.

Following these guidelines will improve the effectiveness of foliar fungicides in managing flax diseases:

- Determine the disease (or diseases) prevalent in the area, and gather information on the disease cycle, such as the presence of primary inoculum.
- Gather information on how flax cultivars react to specific diseases. Then select cultivars that have the best resistance or tolerance to the prevalent diseases.
- Monitor the crop for signs of diseases and environmental factors that favor disease development.
- Determine the economic threshold for each disease and combination of diseases, and apply the appropriate fungicides when the disease level is expected to surpass the economic threshold.
- Follow product label instructions for rates and volumes of water to be applied. Also follow recommendations for postharvest intervals.
- Make more than one application if needed to protect the crop from a disease epidemic.

Fig. 62. Pasmo on flax, affecting the leaves (top), stem (middle), and pods (bottom). (Courtesy Samuel Markell [top and middle] and Michael Wunsch [bottom])

Seed Treatments

Seed treatment fungicides for flax are available, but farmers tend to avoid them because of difficulties in their delivery systems. The waxy mucilage that covers the flax seed makes it difficult for any dry product to stick to the seed before planting. Moreover, the mucilage becomes sticky when wet or under high relative humidity and seeds stick to each other, which makes any liquid seed treatment impossible to handle.

TABLE 12. Flax diseases and their responses to fungicides

Disease(s)	Causal Agent(s)	Comments
Alternaria blight	*Alternaria linicola*	Commonly observed in North America, this disease affects leaves, stems, and seed. Contaminated seed reduces seed quality and can cause seedling blight when used for seeding. Seed treatments are recommended to protect the crop from seedling infections, and foliar applications may prevent leaf and stem infections.
Anthracnose	*Colletotrichum lini*	Anthracnose is primarily a seedborne disease but can be stubble- and soilborne. It is a destructive disease, especially if seed is contaminated. No information on fungicide control is available.
Aster yellows	Phytoplasma	Yellows is a minor disease in flax. This phytoplasma is transmitted by leafhoppers and has a wide host range, including canola, sunflower, sugar beet, carrot, and other plant species. Insecticides used to control leafhoppers may reduce the spread and impact of this disease in flax. Fungicides are not labeled and should not be used for disease management.
Basal stem blight	*Phoma exigua* var. *linicola*	This disease is most damaging to flax at flowering. Elongated, brown lesions form on the stems, and plants turn yellow and die. No information on fungicide control is available.
Boll blight	Extreme heat	Boll blight occurs at the green boll stage, after flowering is complete. Flax bolls wither and die from extreme heat combined with dry weather conditions. Fungicides are not effective in reducing boll blight.
Browning and stem break	*Polyspora lini*	This disease is not widespread in North America, but it can cause significant losses in yield and quality of the flax fiber. Seed treatments may reduce seedling blight, and foliar fungicides may reduce stem break.
Chlorosis	Mineral deficiencies; wet, alkaline soils	Chlorosis is a physiological disorder associated with calcareous soils with unbalanced availability of zinc, manganese, and iron under conditions of high soil moisture. The flax crop may recover when these conditions are alleviated. Foliar application of nutrients may speed up recovery from this disorder, but applying foliar fungicides has no beneficial effect.
Damping-off, root rot, seedling blight	*Alternaria* spp., *Fusarium* spp., *Pythium* spp., *Rhizoctonia solani*	These diseases can be caused by multiple pathogens and result in a significant loss in stand. Yellow-seed cultivars are more susceptible than brown-seed cultivars to most pathogens infecting the seed and seedlings.
Dieback	*Selenophoma linicola*	Dieback, which is observed as the premature ripening and death of plants, is reported infrequently in North America. No information on fungicide efficacy is available.
Fusarium wilt	*Fusarium oxysporum* f. sp. *lini*	This disease is found in all flax-growing areas in North America. All commercial cultivars have moderate to high levels of resistance to the causal agent. Seed treatments may help protect the crop at early stages of growth, but the fungus can infect flax at all growth stages.
Gray mold	*Botrytis cinerea*	Gray mold infects a wide host range of plants. It can be seedborne, causing seedling blight, or airborne, causing leaf and boll blight. Seed treatments may reduce seedling blight, and foliar fungicides may reduce foliage infection and severity.

(continued)

TABLE 12. Continued

Disease(s)	Causal Agent(s)	Comments
Heat and frost cankers	Extreme hot or cold temperatures	These disorders may occur at the seedling stage if the crop is exposed to high temperatures or freezing conditions, thus reducing the stand. Reseeding may be the only option to ensure an acceptable plant population. Fungicides have no effect on these disorders.
Nematode diseases	Several	Several nematodes can cause diseases in flax, but the causal agents differ by region. Fungicides are not labeled for management and should not be used for these diseases.
Pasmo	*Septoria linicola*	Pasmo is the most common flax disease in North America. It infects the leaves, stems, and bolls. Infection starts during the seedling stage and progresses through plant maturity. Seed treatments may reduce seed-to-seedling infections. The application of foliar fungicides likely reduces disease incidence and severity, as well as losses in seed yield and quality.
Powdery mildew	*Oidium lini*	This disease has recently been reported in North America. It is more problematic late in the season, thus resulting in limited losses in yield and quality. Fungicides are effective in reducing the level of disease while protecting yield and seed quality.
Rust	*Melampsora lini*	Flax rust is an aggressive disease that appears as bright-orange pustules on leaves and stems (Fig. 63). It is managed primarily with the use of resistant cultivars. Fungicides can minimize the impact of rust and reduce loss in yield.
Stem twisting and bending	Herbicide damage	Flax is sensitive to damage from several herbicides, especially at early growth stages, and the symptoms may be similar to those of nutrient deficiencies, other disorders, and viral infections. Fungicides are not effective for managing this disorder.
Viruses	Several	Several viruses can cause diseases in flax (such as crinkle and curly top), and the symptoms may be confused with those of fungal diseases. Virus diseases differ by region. Fungicides are not labeled for management and should not be used for these diseases.
White mold (Stem mold or rot)	*Sclerotinia sclerotiorum*	This is a minor disease on flax and may develop when the crop is subjected to saturated soils and lodging. No fungicides effective against the causal agent are currently labeled on flax in the United States.

Fig. 63. Rust on flax. (Courtesy Samuel Markell)

Peanut

Foliar Fungicides

Foliar diseases of peanut—including early and late leaf spot, rust, and web blotch—can be managed with fungicides (Fig. 64). Farmers can also control foliar diseases by following an appropriate crop rotation scheme, using an appropriate peanut cultivar, and adhering to a well-timed fungicide program.

The keys to managing foliar diseases of peanut with fungicides include the following:

- The fungicide program should be initiated before disease becomes established in the field.
- In some areas, disease-forecasting systems are available and farmers can wait until environmental conditions are favorable for disease development before initiating a fungicide program.
- Protectant fungicides (such as chlorothalonil and dodine) are effective when applied before disease is established.

- Applying fungicides with systemic activity (such as quinone outside inhibitors [QoIs] and demethylation inhibitors [DMIs]) should be considered when leaf spot diseases are present. Systemic fungicides will not eliminate these diseases but will slow their development and spread.
- When peanut rust (Fig. 65) is found in a field or environmental conditions are favorable for the development of foliar diseases (for instance, after abundant rainfall), farmers should shorten the interval between fungicide applications and consider the use of systemic fungicides.
- The length of drying time (that is, the time between fungicide application and irrigation or a rainfall event) is critical for fungicide efficacy. If rainfall or irrigation occurs too quickly after a fungicide application, the product may be washed from leaf tissue and another application may be necessary for adequate disease management.
- Fungicide programs for management of foliar diseases should continue to within 2–4 weeks of harvest, depending on current and predicted weather conditions and disease severity in the field.

Peanut farmers are strongly encouraged to practice careful resistance management to prolong the use of currently available fungicides. Because fungicides may be applied more than seven times during a season for management of foliar diseases, selecting fungal

Fig. 64. Early leaf spot on peanut. (Courtesy P. M. Phipps et al.)

Fig. 65. Rust on peanut. (Courtesy Robert C. Kemerait Jr.)

strains resistant to these fungicides poses a significant risk, especially for site-specific fungicides (such as DOIs and DMIs). Resistance by some leaf spot pathogens, such as those that cause early and late leaf spot (Fig. 66), has been documented for tebuconazole, but the impact has been minimal so far.

Fungicides for Control of Soilborne Diseases

Most of the fungicides applied in the middle and late parts of the season are important for managing both foliar and soilborne diseases. Soilborne diseases

Fig. 66. Late leaf spot on peanut. (Courtesy Robert C. Kemerait Jr.)

of peanut—including southern blight, Sclerotinia blight, Rhizoctonia limb rot, and Cylindrocladium black rot (Fig. 67)—can cause significant losses and are particularly difficult to control. Whereas fungicides applied to manage foliar diseases are applied directly to the desired target (the leaves), fungicides applied to manage soilborne diseases must be translocated from the foliage to the limbs and crown of the plant. Because of the difficulty in getting fungicides to the target area, farmers may be able to achieve only 70–80% control of soilborne diseases such as southern blight.

Methods for moving the fungicides from the leaves to the crown include the following:

- Use irrigation or rainfall to redistribute fungicides. However, if fungicides are redistributed too quickly after application, they may not provide adequate protection from leaf spot, and if they are redistributed too slowly, they will not provide adequate soilborne control. The timing of irrigation (or rainfall) can be based on the fungicide drying time, which can vary from 45 minutes for pyraclostrobin to 4 hours for tebuconazole.
- Apply fungicides at night or early in the morning, when the leaves are folded, to increase the amount of fungicide that reaches plant crowns and limbs.
- Increase the spray volume and spray pressure to increase the likelihood that fungicides will penetrate the plant canopy.

Fig. 67. Rhizoctonia limb rot (left) and white mold (right) on peanut. (Courtesy Nicholas S. Dufault)

Fungicide programs for management of soilborne diseases should be initiated when conditions become favorable for disease development. Those conditions include warm soil temperatures and the growth of a plant canopy that traps moisture. In many situations, these conditions develop 45–60 days after planting.

A number of fungicides are currently labeled for the control of soilborne diseases on peanut. However, care should be taken to ensure that the appropriate fungicide is used for the disease of interest. For example, the fungicides used for management of southern blight and Rhizoctonia limb rot are different from those used for management of Sclerotinia blight, and all of these fungicides are different from those used for management of Pythium pod rot.

Making the most of a fungicide application requires an integrated approach:

- Use effective crop rotation and resistant cultivars to reduce disease pressure in a field.
- Consider the impact of weather on both the development of disease and the impact on fungicide efficacy (for example, washing off too quickly, translocating to the crown of the plant).
- Apply fungicides before disease develops.

- Choose a protectant fungicide or a systemic fungicide based on the presence or absence of disease or the threat of disease in a field.

In-Furrow Fungicides

Use of in-furrow fungicides (particularly azoxystrobin) to manage seedling diseases is not a common practice among farmers today, in large part because of the efficacy of seed treatment fungicides to control these diseases. Prothioconazole is currently applied as an in-furrow treatment to manage Cylindrocladium black rot.

Seed Treatments

The use of fungicide seed treatments is critical for the management of seedling diseases on peanut. Seed treatments often include a combination of fungicides to effectively control the complex of pathogens that can cause diseases to the seed and the seedlings. Seed treatments are critical for the management of Aspergillus crown rot and Rhizoctonia seedling disease. They are also important for the management of other seed and seedling disease caused by pathogens from species such as *Rhizopus, Penicillium, Diplodia, Fusarium,* and *Pythium.*

TABLE 13. Peanut diseases and their responses to fungicides		
Disease(s)	**Causal Agent(s)**	**Comments**
Aspergillus crown rot	*Aspergillus niger*	This is typically an early season disease that is observed when conditions are dry and soil temperatures are unusually hot, and it often occurs in conjunction with infestation by the lesser cornstalk borer. In fields where "skippy" plant stands result from severe outbreaks of crown rot, *Tomato spotted wilt virus* is also more severe. Yield losses from crown rot can be severe. Use of a fungicide seed treatment is effective. Irrigation and rainfall can also reduce development of this disease.
Cylindrocladium black rot (CBR)	*Cylindrocladium parasiticum*	CBR is an important disease of peanut, especially in the Virginia–Carolina region and in parts of Georgia and Florida. It is spread by movement of microsclerotia, which can remain viable in the soil for more than 5 years, and it can also be transmitted by planting infected seed. The disease tends to be most severe in years when the conditions at planting are cooler and wetter than normal. CBR is more severe in fields infested with the peanut root-knot nematode and those rotated between peanut and soybean. Management is best achieved by rotation away from peanut and soybean, planting a cultivar with some resistance to CBR, soil fumigation with metam sodium, use of the in-furrow fungicide prothioconazole, and use of a fungicide labeled for suppression of the disease during the season.

(continued)

TABLE 13. Continued

Disease(s)	Causal Agent(s)	Comments
Diplodia collar rot	*Lasiodiplodia theobromae*	Diplodia collar rot occurs sporadically in the southern United States and is often associated with plants growing under stressful conditions or infected with *Tomato spotted wilt virus*. The disease can also be severe on nonstressed plants, especially young plants early in the season. This disease can be transmitted by seed. Management strategies include rotation away from susceptible crops, avoiding use of susceptible peanut cultivars, and applying an effective fungicide.
Early and late leaf spot diseases	*Cercospora arachidicola*, *Cercosporidium personatum*	Although caused by two different fungi, these diseases often occur on the same plants during the same season. Management requires rotation away from peanut, use of resistant cultivars, and implementation of an effective fungicide program that begins before either disease becomes established in the field. Fungicides with systemic activity are recommended in field situations where the diseases are present at the time of application. A management program may include up to seven applications per season. Resistance to demethylation inhibitor (DMI) and methyl benzimidazole carbamate (MBC) fungicides has been reported in some areas.
Nematode diseases	Several	Several nematodes can cause diseases in peanut, but the causal agents differ by region. Fungicides are not labeled for management and should not be used for these diseases.
Peanut pod rot	*Pythium myriotylum*, *Rhizoctonia solani*	Pod rot tends to be more severe in Texas than in the Virginia–Carolina production region. In the U.S. Southeast, pod rot is often associated with an insufficient level of calcium in the soil. This disease complex can be difficult to manage. Successful management requires effective crop rotation, maintenance of soil fertility (especially calcium), and use of fungicides effective against *Pythium* species and *R. solani*.
Rhizoctonia limb rot	*Rhizoctonia solani* AG-4	Caused by the same pathogen as Rhizoctonia seedling disease, limb rot can be a serious problem in some fields, especially those with rank growth and significant rainfall or irrigation. The disease is most often observed as expanding, target-shaped lesions on the stems; it may also affect the pegs (gynophores) just below the soil line or immature pods as they develop. Infected pegs are likely to break at harvest, and mature pods will be lost. Limb rot can be managed with fungicides, but products should be selected carefully, as some are more effective than others.
Rhizoctonia seedling disease	*Rhizoctonia solani* AG-4	This seedling disease is most severe when peanut is planted in cooler and wetter soils than normal and at excessive depths (more than 2–4 inches [5–10 cm]). The risk for disease increases in fields that were previously planted to another crop that is susceptible to *R. solani* AG-4. Fungicide seed treatments are effective against this disease.
Rust	*Puccinia arachidis*	Rust is usually a problem only on peanuts grown in central Florida and along the Gulf Coast. The disease often does not emerge until late in the season and generally has minimal impact on yield. When rust appears earlier in the season (for instance, after a tropical storm), the time between fungicide applications should be reduced (typically, from 14 to 10 days).
Sclerotinia blight	*Sclerotinia minor*	Sclerotinia blight, the official white mold of peanut, is found most commonly in the Virginia–Carolina and Texas production regions. The causal agent survives between seasons as sclerotia. Successful management requires crop rotation, selection of resistant cultivars, and a fungicide program that includes an active ingredient that is effective against basidiomycetes.

(continued)

TABLE 13. Continued

Disease(s)	Causal Agent(s)	Comments
Seed and seedling rots	*Fusarium* spp., *Penicillium* spp., *Rhizopus* spp., *Aspergillus* spp., *Pythium* spp., *Diplodia* spp.	Germinating peanut seeds are prone to fungal infections. Planting high-quality seed and adding seed treatment fungicides can help manage these diseases.
Southern blight	*Sclerotium rolfsii*	Southern blight is commonly known as white mold in the southern production region (although this is not an official name). The causal agent survives as sclerotia in the soil. Disease typically develops in warm soils and when the peanut canopy traps enough moisture to facilitate fungal growth. Fungicide programs to manage stem rot typically begin 45–60 days after planting and continue through much of the season. One of the greatest difficulties in managing this disease is that fungicides are applied to the foliage. Applying them to the stems or crowns can enhance their effectiveness. Early season applications of prothioconazole (14–35 days after planting) may also provide effective control of this disease.
Verticillium wilt	*Verticillium dahliae*	No effective cultural or fungicidal controls are currently available for this disease. Should a field become infested, long rotations with nonhost crops (such as corn, sorghum, and Sudangrass) may be effective in reducing the level of inoculum. Other susceptible crops (such as cotton and potato) should be avoided as rotational crops.
Viruses	Several	Several viruses can cause diseases in peanut, and the symptoms may be confused with those of fungal diseases. Virus diseases differ by region. Fungicides are not labeled for management and should not be used for these diseases.
Web blotch	*Phoma arachidicola*	This foliar disease is a problem primarily in Virginia and North Carolina. It can be managed effectively with a standard fungicide program. When web blotch and leaf spot diseases occur together, the fungicide that is applied should be effective against all of these diseases.

Potato

Foliar Fungicides

Applying foliar fungicides is a standard practice in potato production. The fungicide used and frequency of application may vary by region and year of production. Typically, the first application of foliar fungicide is made just prior to canopy closure or when potato physiological days (P-days) reach 300 (Johnson et al., 1986). After that, applications are made on a 7-, 10-, or 14-day schedule, depending on environmental conditions and disease pressure. The health of the plant canopy is critical in producing tuber bulk and quality. Integrated pest management and disease-forecasting tools such as Blitecast, which forecasts development of potato late blight, are frequently used to aid in the timing of fungicide applications.

In-Furrow or At-Planting Fungicide Treatments

In some regions of the United States, farmers have adopted at-planting or in-furrow fungicide treatments. The compounds typically selected for in-furrow treatments have some systemic activity and can aid in protecting the emerging seedlings when environmental conditions are wet and cool and thus favorable for disease development. Both fungi and oomycetes can be managed with in-furrow treatments.

Seed Treatments

Seed treatments are commonly used for commercial potato production and include compounds such as fludioxonil and mancozeb. One of the target diseases of seed treatments for potato is Rhizoctonia stem canker and black scurf. Another target disease is late blight of potato. When late blight is a risk on seed, seed treatments with mancozeb compounds or cymoxanil can be very effective in managing the disease.

TABLE 14. Potato diseases and their responses to fungicides

Disease(s)	Causal Agent(s)	Comments
Bacterial soft rot	*Pectobacterium carotovorum* var. *carotovorum*	This disease is caused by a soil- or seedborne pathogen that thrives on low oxygen conditions (for example, at the center of a pile of stored tubers). Disease development is favored by high temperatures and high levels of soil moisture. It can be limited with cultural practices by managing field moisture and providing appropriate airflow in storage. Fungicides are not labeled and should not be used for management.
Black dot	*Colletotrichum coccodes*	Black dot is a foliar and tuber blemish disease; the tuber phase is often misdiagnosed as silver scurf. Applying foliar fungicides and reducing crop stresses (such as irrigation deficit) both aid in disease control.
Black leg	*Pectobacterium carotovorum* var. *atrosepticum*	Inoculum comes primarily from infected seed tubers but may also be spread in infested soil, in contaminated irrigation water, and by insects. Development of black leg is favored by cool, wet conditions at planting followed by high temperatures after seedling emergence. Fungicides are not labeled and should not be used for management.
Brown spot	*Alternaria alternata*	Brown spot can be present with early blight in a complex of early blight disease. The disease is likely controlled by the foliar fungicides that are usually applied to control early blight. The causal agent of brown spot is typically a weaker pathogen (often referred to as a secondary invader) that follows infection by another more aggressive pathogen.

(continued)

TABLE 14. Continued

Disease(s)	Causal Agent(s)	Comments
Common scab	*Streptomyces scabies*	This disease causes tuber blemishes, and the lesions can be superficial or pitted. The causal agent can survive in the soil or be seedborne. Strategies for disease management include adequate irrigation at tuberization, maintaining the soil pH below 5.2, using resistant cultivars, and applying fungicides at planting. Some soil fumigants can limit symptoms of common scab on potato tubers.
Early blight	*Alternaria solani*	Early blight is primarily a foliar disease, but it can also cause symptoms on tubers (Fig. 68). The causal agent persists in field residue, and it can potentially defoliate plants of susceptible cultivars. Fungicides are effective for management, and in some regions, applications are necessary from canopy closure to vine kill.
Early dying complex	*Verticillium dahliae*, root lesion nematode (*Pratylenchus penetrans*)	Both the fungal and nematode pathogens of this disease complex are soilborne and persist over time. Symptoms include the yellowing of plants and the death of individual stems. Plants may also senesce 1 or more weeks earlier than normal, if the level of disease is high. Some resistant cultivars are available. In certain regions, soil fumigation is necessary to prevent yield losses.
Fusarium dry rot	*Fusarium sambucinum*	This soilborne pathogen causes a postharvest disease of stored tubers. Some postharvest fungicide treatments are effective against this Fusarium disease.
Late blight	*Phytophthora infestans*	Late blight affects both foliage and tubers (Fig. 69). The causal agent can be seedborne (culls, seed, volunteers) but is currently not known to be soilborne in the United States. A few commercial cultivars have resistance, although it may not be complete. Fungicides are necessary to effectively manage this disease and must be applied preventively and repeatedly to maintain control. Good control of solanaceous weeds is also important. Disease-forecasting programs (such as Blitecast) can aid in the proper timing of fungicide applications.

Fig. 68. Early blight of potato. (Courtesy Amanda J. Gevens)

Fig. 69. Late blight of potato. (Courtesy Amanda J. Gevens)

(continued)

TABLE 14. Continued

Disease(s)	Causal Agent(s)	Comments
Nematode diseases	Several	Several nematodes can cause diseases in potato (for instance, early dying complex), but the causal agents differ by region. Fungicides are not labeled for management and should not be used for these diseases.
Pink rot	*Phytophthora erythroseptica*	Pink rot is a tuber disease. Infection typically begins in the field under conditions of high soil moisture, and symptoms can develop at harvest or postharvest. Application of phosphorous acids during the production season or as a postharvest treatment can be effective in managing this disease. Several fungicides with activity on oomycetes can aid in management when applied at planting, during the production season, or at postharvest (as labels allow).
Powdery scab	*Spongospora subterranea*	The causal agent of powdery scab (Fig. 70) can be seedborne or soilborne. Some resistant cultivars are available. Fumigation treatments before planting and fungicide applications at planting can provide some control of the disease. Long crop rotations and delaying planting to avoid cool, wet soils may also aid in control.
Rhizoctonia stem canker and black scurf	*Rhizoctonia solani*	Good field sanitation and harvesting at maturity help limit this foliar and tuber blemish disease. Fungicides applied as seed treatments or in-furrow treatments at planting can also provide effective management.
Silver scurf	*Helminthosporium solani*	This soilborne pathogen can cause infection in the field or in postharvest storage. Symptoms are often not visible until after harvest, when conditions in storage are excessively moist. Silver scurf can be controlled by making certain that tuber periderm is mature and that tubers do not remain in moist soil for a prolonged period beyond vine kill. Postharvest applications of phosphorous acids can reduce damage from this disease, and management of air temperature, air movement, and humidity in storage can limit its progress.
Viruses	Several	Several viruses can cause diseases in potato, and the symptoms may be confused with those of fungal diseases. Virus diseases differ by region. Fungicides are not labeled for management and should not be used for these diseases.
White mold	*Sclerotinia sclerotiorum*	White mold occurs sporadically on potato. It is particularly problematic in years when precipitation is frequent, leaving foliage wet for prolonged periods. Fungicides can be useful in managing the disease if applied before or at the time of infection.

Fig. 70. Powdery scab on potato. (Courtesy Amanda J. Gevens)

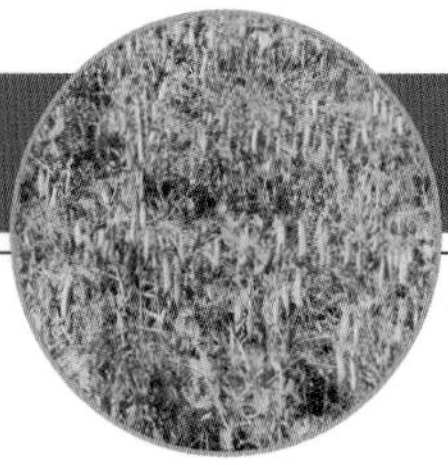

Pulse Crops (Chickpea, Lentil, and Field Pea)

Foliar Fungicides

Many of the most serious diseases of the cool-season pulse crops—such as Ascochyta blight on chickpea (Fig. 71), anthracnose on lentil, and Sclerotinia stem rot on lentil—cannot be successfully managed with fungicides alone. All available management tools must be used, including crop rotation and, when available, host resistance.

Two different approaches can be considered for using fungicides to manage Ascochyta blight on chickpea:

- A preventive approach is generally recommended. A preventive application of chlorothalonil is advised if no disease has been detected 7–10 days before bloom initiation and there have been frequent rain events or heavy dew or conditions are dry at bloom initiation. Then, 7–10 days after applying chlorothalonil, systemic fungicides should be applied.
- If a preventive approach is not taken, fields should be scouted carefully, beginning in the late stages of vegetative growth (approximately 2 weeks prior to bloom). When scouting, individuals should walk in a zigzag pattern through the field, stopping at multiple points and examining the bottom one-third of the canopy for lesions. If trace levels of Ascochyta blight are found, applications of systemic fungicides should begin. Sequential applications should be made 10–14 days apart during the critical bloom and pod-fill stages. Even if disease is at a low level at the end of bloom, a fungicide application may be necessary during the pod-fill stage. The incidence of pod infection can be high, despite a low level of foliar disease. When pods become infected, they often do not produce seeds.

A preventive approach is also recommended to manage diseases of lentil, such as anthracnose (Fig. 72), Ascochyta blight, Botrytis gray mold, and Sclerotinia stem rot. Fungicides will not be very effective if applications are delayed until disease has reached a moderate or high level. If conditions are favorable for disease development, a fungicide application is generally recommended at bloom or just prior to canopy closure. If wet weather persists, a second application may be necessary 7–14 days later. Farmers should keep in mind that fungicides differ in their effectiveness against these diseases, and a fungicide with efficacy against one disease may not be effective against other diseases. Products should be chosen on the basis of scouting reports and the history of a field.

Some diseases may be more severe when crop rotations are short or when lentil, field pea, or chickpea is planted immediately adjacent to a field where the same crop was grown the previous year. For most diseases, a minimum 2- to 3-year rotation is needed. Certain fungal diseases of the cool-season pulses, including Ascochyta blight and anthracnose, are host specific. For example, *Ascochyta lentis* and *Colletotrichum truncatum* cause disease on lentil but not on field pea or chickpea. Other diseases—such as Botrytis gray mold, Sclerotinia stem rot, many root rots and

Fig. 71. Ascochyta blight on chickpea. (Courtesy Kiersten A. Wise)

seedling blights, and most viral diseases—are problems on chickpea, lentil, and field pea. The sequential planting of two different cool-season pulses (for example, chickpea followed by lentil) can facilitate the buildup of pathogen populations for the diseases that are not host specific.

Anthracnose (lentil), Ascochyta blight (chickpea and lentil), Mycosphaerella blight (field pea), and Botrytis gray mold (chickpea, lentil, and field pea) are all at high risk for developing fungicide resistance. The pathogen that causes Ascochyta blight of chickpea (*A. rabiei*) has already developed resistance to quinone outside inhibitor (QoI) fungicides (Wise et al., 2009). Similarly, the causal agent of Botrytis gray mold (*Botrytis cinerea*) has developed resistance to QoI and succinate dehydrogenase inhibitor (SDHI) fungicides in other cropping systems (Bardas et al., 2010; Kim and Xiao, 2010). To prevent the development of fungicide resistance, fungicide chemistries should be rotated within and across growing seasons and products should not be applied below the labeled rates.

Most of the foliar fungal diseases that affect cool-season pulses not only reduce yield but also contribute to seed-quality issues, such as discoloration. Applications of foliar fungicides can help alleviate both problems.

Seed Treatments

Seed treatments are widely used for protection against seed-to-seedling transmission of foliar diseases from infested seed. Seed treatments are used to reduce seed-to-seedling transmission of Alternaria blight (chickpea), Ascochyta blight (chickpea and lentil), Mycosphaerella blight (field pea), and Botrytis gray mold (chickpea, lentil, and field pea).

Seed-to-seedling transmission is important for many foliar diseases, and the use of clean seed is essential. Following these seed infection thresholds is advised:

- 0% for Ascochyta blight of chickpea and lentil in humid regions
- 5% for Ascochyta blight of lentil in dry regions
- 10% for Mycosphaerella blight of field pea

Fig. 72. Anthracnose on lentil. (Courtesy Michael Wunsch)

For Ascochyta blight of chickpea, seed treatment is advised even when a seed lot tests negative for the pathogen, because virtually no seed lot is completely free of Ascochyta-infected seeds. On lentil and chickpea, seed-to-seedling transmission of the causal agent of Botrytis gray mold (*B. cinerea*) can result in economically damaging levels of Botrytis seedling blight. A threshold for Botrytis seed infection has not been established for the United States and Canada, but it may be advisable to avoid planting lentil and chickpea seed with an elevated incidence of Botrytis infection (Fig. 73).

Fungicides that provide protection against seed decay and damping-off are not always effective at protecting against seed-to-seedling transmission of foliar diseases. Thus, the use of multiple fungicides is often necessary when treating seeds.

Fig. 73. Botrytis infection on lentil. (Courtesy Michael Wunsch)

TABLE 15. Pulse crop diseases and their responses to fungicides

Disease(s)	Causal Agent(s)	Crop(s)[a]	Comments
Alternaria blight	*Alternaria alternata*	C, L, P	Seed treatments can reduce transmission of this seedborne pathogen. Foliar fungicides may be effective on susceptible cultivars of chickpea. On lentil and field pea, the disease is minor and fungicides are not likely needed.
Anthracnose	*Colletotrichum truncatum* (L, P), *C. pisi* (P)	L, P	On lentil, anthracnose disease is easily confused with Ascochyta blight. Host resistance is available for only one of the two races of the causal agent. Because both races are widely distributed in the northern Great Plains of the United States and Canada, resistance to one race does not necessarily predict field performance of cultivars. Fungicide applications are often critical to disease management. In field pea, anthracnose is a minor disease and fungicides are not likely needed.
Aphanomyces root rot	*Aphanomyces euteiches*	L, P	Development of this disease is favored by cool weather and saturated soils. It can be managed with long crop rotations. Seed treatments and foliar fungicide applications are generally ineffective.
Ascochyta blight	*Ascochyta rabiei* (C), *A. lentis* (L), various pathogens (P)	C, L, P	Ascochyta blight can cause complete crop failure in chickpea. The causal agents are seedborne in chickpea and lentil, so seed treatments can reduce transmission. In chickpea, applications of foliar fungicides are often critical even on cultivars with partial resistance. In many regions, quinone outside inhibitor (QoI) fungicides are no longer effective, because the pathogens have developed resistance to them. Lentil cultivars with moderate resistance are available. Foliar fungicides may be necessary for lentil; QoI fungicides remain effective for this crop. (For field pea, see Mycosphaerella blight.)

[a] C = chickpea, L = lentil, P = field pea.

(continued)

TABLE 15. Continued

Disease(s)	Causal Agent(s)	Crop(s)[a]	Comments
Bacterial blight	*Xanthomonas campestris* pv. *cassiae* (C), *Pseudomonas syringae* pv. *pisi* (P)	C, P	In chickpea, disease development is favored by warm (85°F [29°C]), wet weather; crop rotation and other cultural methods are effective for management. In field pea, the causal agent is seedborne, and disease development is favored by wet weather and mechanical damage. Disease can be severe after hail events and should be managed with clean seed and resistant varieties. Fungicides are not labeled and should not be used for management.
Botrytis gray mold	*Botrytis cinerea*	C, L, P	Botrytis gray mold is particularly damaging when flowering and pod set coincide with wet weather. Applications of foliar fungicides can be critical to management. In lentil and chickpea, the disease also occurs as a seedling blight, which is best managed with clean seed and seed treatments.
Brown spot	*Pseudomonas syringae* pv. *syringae*	P	Brown spot is very similar to bacterial blight. The causal agent is seedborne and seed transmitted, and the development of disease is favored by mechanical damage and wet weather. Fungicides are not labeled and should not be used for management.
Downy mildew	*Peronospora viciae* (L, P), *P. ciceris* (C), *P. lentis* (L)	C, L, P	In field pea, this disease can be severe in cool, wet weather. It is managed most effectively in field pea with crop rotation, seed treatments, and tolerant cultivars; however, foliar fungicides are available for use. Resistance to metalaxyl has been reported in many regions. In chickpea and lentil, downy mildew is generally a minor disease but can be significant in cool, wet weather. This disease has not yet been reported in the United States or Canada on chickpea and lentil. Foliar fungicides may be useful in management.
Fusarium root rot	*Fusarium* spp.	C, L, P	Fusarium root rot is distinct from Fusarium wilt. Fusarium root rot is managed with long crop rotations and good fertility. Foliar fungicides are not effective on this disease, and seed treatments are generally ineffective, as well.
Fusarium wilt	*Fusarium oxysporum* f. sp. *ciceris* (C), *F. oxysporum* f. sp. *lentis* (L), *F. oxysporum* f. sp. *pisi* (P)	C, L, P	This soilborne disease causes wilt that is most severe in warm, dry weather. It can be managed by using resistant cultivars. Foliar fungicides have no efficacy against Fusarium wilt, but seed treatments can reduce contamination of the seed by the causal agent.
Macrophomina root rot	*Macrophomina phaseolina*	C, L	Macrophomina root rot is favored by hot, dry weather. Late plantings should be avoided. Seed treatments are effective against the infection of seedlings.
Mycosphaerella blight (Ascochyta blight)	*Ascochyta pisi*, *A. pinodes* (*Didymella pinodes*, *Mycosphaerella pinodes*), *Phoma medicaginis* var. *pinodella*	P	These pathogens are seedborne, so seed treatments can reduce transmission. The level of disease can be severe when cool, wet weather occurs during bloom and pod fill. Foliar fungicides are effective in management, but the timing of application is important. If conditions favor disease, the optimal fungicide timing is bloom initiation. Obtaining good coverage is difficult with later applications. Note that the disease level must be high for fungicide applications to increase the chances of an economic return.
Nematode diseases	Several	C, L, P	Several nematodes can cause diseases in pulse crops, but the causal agents differ by region and crop. Fungicides are not labeled for management and should not be used for these diseases.

(continued)

TABLE 15. Continued

Disease(s)	Causal Agent(s)	Crop(s)[a]	Comments
Phytophthora root rot	*Phytophthora medicaginis*	C	This disease is problematic on chickpea from emergence to near maturity and is most severe when soils become saturated. Seed treatments provide protection only during the seedling stage, and foliar fungicides are not effective.
Powdery mildew	*Erysiphe* spp., *Leveillula* spp. (C, L), *E. pisi*, *E. trifolii* (P)	C, L, P	Powdery mildew is most severe at flowering and pod set in chickpea and lentil. In chickpea, it is generally a minor disease, and fungicides can be useful for management. In field pea (Fig. 74), the disease can be managed with host resistance, but fungicides can be useful when susceptible cultivars are grown. Disease is most likely to develop when the days are warm and dry but the dew point is reached at night. If weather conditions are favorable and a susceptible cultivar is being grown, fungicides should be applied immediately after the first appearance of symptoms of powdery mildew. Fungicides are not effective once the disease has reached a moderate to high level of severity.
Pythium root and seedling rot	*Pythium* spp.	C, L, P	This disease is most severe in cool, wet soils. Seed treatments are effective, but foliar fungicides are not.
Rhizoctonia root rot	*Rhizoctonia solani*	C, L, P	Rhizoctonia root rot can be severe in compacted soils. Seed treatments provide partial control, but foliar fungicides are not effective.
Rust	*Uromyces viciae-fabae* (L), *U. fabae* (P)	L, P	Lentil rust, which can result in complete crop failure, has not yet been reported in the United States or Canada. The disease is best managed with resistant cultivars, but fungicides are also effective. Rust is generally a minor disease of field pea, but fungicides are effective for management (Fig. 75).
Sclerotinia stem rot	*Sclerotinia sclerotiorum*, *S. minor* (C), *S. trifoliorum* (C)	C, L, P	This disease can be a serious problem on lentil and field pea when cool, wet weather occurs during middle to late bloom and pod set. Fungicides provide only partial disease control on lentil and field pea but can be effective when applied preventively. Sclerotinia stem rot is a minor disease on chickpea; development is favored by cool, moist weather. On chickpea, this disease rarely requires treatment with fungicides. Fungicides control only foliar infections on chickpea, not crown infections.

Fig. 74. Powdery mildew on field pea. (Courtesy Samuel Markell)

Fig. 75. Rust on field pea. (Courtesy Samuel Markell)

(continued)

TABLE 15. Continued

Disease(s)	Causal Agent(s)	Crop(s)[a]	Comments
Sclerotinia stem rot	*Sclerotinia sclerotiorum*, *S. minor* (C), *S. trifoliorum* (C)	C, L, P	This disease can be a serious problem on lentil and field pea when cool, wet weather occurs during middle to late bloom and pod set. Fungicides provide only partial disease control on lentil and field pea but can be effective when applied preventively. Sclerotinia stem rot is a minor disease on chickpea; development is favored by cool, moist weather. On chickpea, this disease rarely requires treatment with fungicides. Fungicides control only foliar infections on chickpea, not crown infections.
Stemphylium blight	*Stemphylium botryosum*	L	Stemphylium blight is a disease of maturing lentil. It can be severe when rains occur at late bloom or pod fill. Fungicides can be effective for management. If weather is favorable for disease development and a susceptible cultivar is being grown, fungicides should be applied immediately after the first appearance of symptoms. Fungicides are not effective once the disease has become established.
Thielaviopsis root rot	*Thielaviopsis basicola*	C, L, P	Crop rotation can help delay the buildup of pathogen populations. Seed treatments and foliar fungicides are not effective.
Verticillium wilt	*Verticillium albo-atrum*	C, L	This is a minor disease that causes yellowing of leaves and wilt. Foliar fungicides are not effective.
Viruses	Several	C, L, P	Several viruses can cause diseases in pulse crops (including alfalfa mosaic, bean leaf roll, bean yellow mosaic, pea enation mosaic, and pea streak), and the symptoms may be confused with those of fungal diseases. Virus diseases differ by region. Fungicides are not labeled for management and should not be used for these diseases.

Rice

Disease management in rice production is critical to maximize yield potential and quality. Rice can be affected by many types of disease-causing organisms (including oomycetes, fungi, and bacteria), depending on the environmental conditions in a given year or geographical region. Some of the most costly diseases affecting U.S. rice production include rice blast, sheath blight, bacterial panicle blight, stem rot, and kernel and false smut.

The use of fungicides is a key component in managing rice diseases, but fungicides are not effective on all diseases. To manage rice diseases effectively, fungicides should be used as part of an integrated disease management program that includes plant resistance, fertility management, and cultural practices.

Foliar Fungicides

The use of foliar fungicides for rice blast and sheath blight (Fig. 76) is justified in many cases. Circumstances in which fungicide application may be economically beneficial include the following:

- The field has a history of disease.
- A susceptible cultivar has been planted.
- The crop has a high yield potential.
- The rice is being grown for seed.

Fig. 76. Sheath blight on rice. (Courtesy Donald Groth, Louisiana State University AgCenter, Bugwood.org)

- The field was planted late. (Late-planted rice is more likely to develop foliar diseases.)
- The market price for rice is high.

Sheath blight, rice blast, and narrow brown leaf spot are all economically important rice diseases in Arkansas, Louisiana, and Mississippi. Recommendations for fungicide use are as follow:

- **Sheath blight:** Cultivars that are susceptible or very susceptible will experience economic loss if 5–10% of the tillers are infected during the vegetative growth stages, and for moderately susceptible cultivars, the level increases to 15%. At these levels of infection, fungicide use should be considered.
- **Blast:** When symptoms of leaf blast are present, a foliar fungicide should be applied at early heading (when 50–70% of heads have emerged). Leaf blast does not always precede rotten neck blast, and preventive applications of fungicide may be necessary if a blast-susceptible cultivar is being grown. The incidence and severity of blast increases when plants are stressed (for instance, because of loss of flood, fertility imbalance, etc.). Under severe conditions, two fungicide applications may be needed, with the first application at late boot to boot split (5% heading).
- **Narrow brown leaf spot:** Fungicides are most effective when applied between the boot and heading growth stages.

Seed Treatments

Most commercially available rice cultivars come pretreated with a fungicide seed treatment package that includes more than one active ingredient. A typical fungicide seed treatment package contains a metalaxyl- or mefenoxam-based active ingredient for control of *Pythium* species and a quinone outside inhibitor (QoI) component for control of *Rhizoctonia* species.

Treating seed with fungicides is recommended when planting into clay soils, when reduced-till or no-till farming is the predominant practice, or when a history of poor seedling emergence or seedling diseases has been documented. Seed treatments should also be applied to prevent damping-off and seed rot in situations where rice will be water seeded. Depending on the product applied, seed treatments can guard against Fusarium-based seedling disease and seedling blights caused by additional fungi.

TABLE 16. Rice diseases and their responses to fungicides

Disease(s)	Causal Agent(s)	Comments
Bacterial panicle blight	*Burkholderia glumae*	Some cultivars have more resistance to this disease than others. Crops planted late in the season and fertilized with high nitrogen rates tend to have more disease. Fungicides are not labeled and should not be used for management.
Blast	*Pyricularia oryzae*	For the leaf stages of blast, infection levels tend to be less severe when floodwater is consistently maintained at adequate depths. The disease can also be managed by planting cultivars resistant to prevalent races of the fungus and avoiding excessive rates of nitrogen. (Nitrogen amounts vary with cropping history, soil type, varieties, and so on.) Draining for straighthead disorder or water weevil control may increase the incidence and severity of blast, and the disease is normally worse on late-planted rice. The use of fungicides will help manage this disease if applied at the proper growth stages.
Brown leaf spot	*Bipolaris oryzae*	A low level of potassium in the soil increases susceptibility to infection by this causal agent. Ideal growing conditions should be maintained through fertilization, land leveling, proper soil preparation, and other cultural practices. Foliar fungicides can effectively manage the disease, and seed-protectant fungicides can reduce the severity of seedling blight caused by the fungus.
Kernel and false smut	*Tilletia barclayana,* *Ustilaginoidea virens*	Disease development (Fig. 77) is favored by a high nitrogen level. Some cultivars appear less susceptible than others. Fungicides containing propiconazole reduce disease, but the timing of application is critical.
Narrow brown leaf spot	*Cercospora oryzae*	The use of resistant cultivars offers the best approach for management of narrow brown leaf spot, but fungicides may control the disease. Fungicides containing propiconazole have the most effective activity, but they cannot be applied to the second (ratoon) crop.
Nematode diseases	Several	Several nematodes can cause diseases in rice, but the causal agents differ by region. Fungicides are not labeled for management and should not be used for these diseases.
Seed and seedling diseases	*Pythium* spp., *Achlya* spp., *Rhizoctonia* spp., *Fusarium* spp., others	Seeding into clear water reduces the incidence of oomycetes. Most dry-seeded rice seed is treated with a combination of fungicides to improve the spectrum of disease control.

Fig. 77. False smut on rice. (Courtesy Yulin Jia)

(continued)

TABLE 16. Continued

Disease(s)	Causal Agent(s)	Comments
Sheath blight	*Rhizoctonia solani*	Thick stands and excessive nitrogen applications tend to favor the development of sheath blight. Fungicide applications may be necessary to suppress disease. Resistance to quinone outside inhibitor (QoI) fungicides has been reported in some areas.
Stem rot	*Sclerotium oryzae*	Applications of potassium to the soil may reduce disease severity in instances where the level of this nutrient is inadequate. Certain fungicides have activity against this causal agent but are not considered economical compared to applying potassium.
Straighthead	Physiological disorder	To prevent this disorder, water should be drained from the field just before the jointing stage of growth. Water should be left off the field until cracks form, and then the field should be reflooded. Fungicides are not labeled and should not be used for management.
Viruses	Several	Several viruses can cause diseases in rice, and the symptoms may be confused with those of fungal diseases. Virus diseases differ by region. Fungicides are not labeled for management and should not be used for these diseases.

Small Grains
(Barley and Wheat)

Foliar Fungicides

The use of fungicides for disease management in wheat and barley has increased dramatically since 2000. This increase was stimulated by the combination of three factors: frequent problems with disease, the increased value of grain, and the reduced costs of fungicides.

Determining if a fungicide is needed to protect a crop from disease can be difficult. By using the information that is available before application, however, it is possible to improve the chances of producing a desirable yield response. Following these guidelines will help farmers evaluate the need for applying foliar fungicides:

- Use information about a specific cultivar's disease reaction to establish priorities before purchasing seed. Information about a cultivar's genetic resistance or susceptibility to disease is often available from universities and seed companies. Research indicates that cultivars susceptible to the most frequent and damaging diseases within a region are more likely to benefit from the extra disease protection offered by a fungicide. Cultivars resistant to these diseases normally do not need fungicide treatments to maintain their yield potentials.
- Use information about the risk of disease to refine the decision. Two important indicators of disease risk are (1) state and regional reports of disease outbreaks and (2) the presence of disease within a field before the heading stages of growth. The largest and most consistent yield responses to fungicides occur when susceptible

cultivars are combined with scenarios involving high disease risk and high yield. The need for a fungicide is reduced when disease-resistant cultivars are grown, when the risk of disease is low, or when the yield potential is low.

- Consider yield potential and weather before making the final decision to apply a fungicide. Fields with good yield potential at the time of application and those intended for seed production are both high priorities for fungicide application. These priorities are reinforced when weather forecasts indicate conditions are likely to continue to remain favorable for disease development. Production problems such as drought, viral or bacterial diseases, and insect pressure may lower yield potential and reduce the need for the additional costs associated with fungicide applications.

Seed Treatments

Fungicide seed treatments are used as part of a management plan for seedling and seedborne diseases, including common bunt and loose smut (Fig. 78). The most effective fungicides are products containing a combination of active ingredients that are effective against a wide spectrum of fungi (including *Fusarium, Tilletia,* and *Ustilago* species) and oomycetes (such as *Pythium* species).

Fig. 78. Loose smut on wheat. (Courtesy Vivek Gupta)

TABLE 17. Small grain diseases and their responses to fungicides

Disease(s)	Causal Agent(s)	Crop(s)[a]	Comments
Bacterial leaf streak and black chaff	*Xanthomonas campestris* pv. *undulosa* (W), *X. campestris* pv. *translucens* (B)	B, W	These bacterial diseases can be confused with leaf diseases. Fungicides are not labeled for bacterial leaf streak and black chaff and should not be used for management.
Black head molds (sooty molds)	*Cladosporium* spp., *Alternaria* spp.	B, W	So-called sooty molds are late-season diseases associated with rain and humid weather, and they develop near maturity of the crop. They are generally not considered serious threats to yield. Fungicides are not labeled for management.
Common bunt (stinking smut)	*Tilletia caries, T. laevis*	B, W	These fungi produce a strong fishy odor. The disease is spread through contamination of seed and can be managed effectively with fungicide seed treatments.
Covered smut	*Ustilago hordei*	B	This seedborne fungus is spread through contaminated seed and can be managed effectively with fungicide seed treatments.
Ergot	*Claviceps purpurea*	B, W	Ergot is rare in wheat. When it occurs, infection develops in the early stages of grain development. Fungicides are not labeled for management.
Fusarium head blight	*Fusarium graminearum, Fusarium* spp.	B, W	Fusarium head blight is also referred to as scab (Fig. 79). Infection develops following head emergence or during the early stages of grain development. Fungicides must be applied to the heads to be effective in management. Demethylation inhibitors (DMIs) provide disease suppression, but most products containing quinone outside inhibitors (QoIs) are not labeled for postheading application and are not recommended for use.
Loose smut	*Ustilago tritici*	B, W	This fungus, which is seedborne, infects the kernels during the early stages of grain development. The disease is best managed with seed treatments using systemic fungicides.

Fig. 79. Fusarium head blight (scab) on wheat. (Courtesy Marcia McMullen)

[a] B = barley, W = wheat.

(continued)

TABLE 17. Continued

Disease(s)	Causal Agent(s)	Crop(s)[a]	Comments
Nematode diseases	Several	B, W	Several nematodes can cause diseases in small grains, but the causal agents differ by region. Fungicides are not labeled for management and should not be used for these diseases.
Net blotch and spot form of net blotch	*Pyrenophora teres* f. sp. *teres*, *P. teres* f. sp. *maculata*	B	These fungi survive on crop residue and may also be seedborne. The disease (Fig. 80) can be managed using crop rotation, genetic resistance, and foliar fungicides.
Powdery mildew	*Blumeria graminis* f. sp. *tritici* (W), *B. graminis* f. sp. *hordei* (B)	B, W	Powdery mildew is most common in cool, wet environments. The disease is managed primarily with genetic resistance, but fungicide applications reduce the risk of severe yield losses in susceptible cultivars.
Root rot	*Cochliobolus sativus*, *Gaeumannomyces graminis*, *Fusarium* spp., *Rhizoctonia* spp.	B, W	This disease is most common in continuous small grains or in fields with grassy weed problems. Some seed treatment fungicides are labeled for *Fusarium* and *Rhizoctonia* species but often only for suppression.
Rusts (leaf rust, stripe rust, and stem rust)	*Puccinia triticina* (W), *P. hordei* (B), *P. striiformis*, *P. graminis*	B, W	Stem rust is currently rare in North America, but leaf rust (Fig. 81) and stripe rust (Fig. 82) can be problematic nearly everywhere that small grains are grown. These diseases are often managed with genetic resistance; fungicides may be needed to prevent yield losses with susceptible cultivars.

Fig. 80. Net blotch on barley. (Courtesy Marcia McMullen)

Fig. 81. Leaf rust on wheat. (Courtesy Kiersten A. Wise)

Fig. 82. Stripe rust on wheat. (Courtesy John Youmans)

(continued)

TABLE 17. Continued

Disease(s)	Causal Agent(s)	Crop(s)[a]	Comments
Seedling blights	*Fusarium* spp., *Pythium* spp., *Rhizoctonia* spp.	B, W	Seed treatment with fungicides generally provides protection from seedling diseases.
Septoria tritici blotch, Speckled leaf blotch	*Septoria tritici* (W), *Septoria passerinii* (B), *Stagonospora avenae* f. sp. *triticea* (B)	B, W	The *Septoria* fungus survives in crop residue but is moved efficiently by wind, reducing the effectiveness of crop rotation as a management strategy. The disease is favored by frequent rainfall and can be managed effectively with fungicide applications.
Spot blotch	*Cochliobolus sativus*	B, W	The fungus that causes spot blotch can survive in soil, on seed, and in residue from previous barley or wheat crops. The disease is normally managed through crop rotation and genetic resistance. Foliar fungicides are also effective for management.
Stagonospora nodorum leaf and glume blotch	*Stagonospora nodorum* (B, W), *S. avenae* f. sp. *triticea* (B)	B, W	This fungal disease survives in crop residue but can also be moved on infected seed. Seed treatment with fungicides reduces the risk of seed transmission, and applications of foliar fungicides are effective for managing disease on leaves and heads. Management of glume blotch requires applying fungicides to heads.
Tan spot	*Pyrenophora tritici-repentis*	W	This fungus survives in residue from previous wheat crops. The disease is normally managed through crop rotation and genetic resistance in some wheat classes. Foliar fungicides also are effective for management of tan spot.
Viruses	Several	B, W	Several viruses can cause diseases in small grains, and the symptoms may be confused with those of fungal diseases. Virus diseases differ by region. Fungicides are not labeled for management and should not be used for these diseases.

Sorghum

and no yield advantage has occurred in the absence of disease.

Fungicides are used in hybrid seed production to manage ergot, since male sterile parents are particularly susceptible to this disease. Ergot management in commercial production fields is not currently recommended.

Foliar Fungicides

Foliar fungal diseases on sorghum can be managed using a combination of methods, including resistant hybrids, crop rotation, tillage, and foliar fungicides. Foliar fungicides have been used on this crop on only a limited basis because of low commodity prices and the lack of disease pressure in major production areas. Only a few university trials have been reported,

Seed Treatments

Except for organic production, most grain sorghum is treated with a fungicide seed treatment. Commercially available seed treatments typically contain two or more active ingredients that are effective against fungi (including *Fusarium* and *Rhizoctonia* species) and oomycetes (including *Pythium* and *Peronosclerospora* species).

TABLE 18. Sorghum diseases and their responses to fungicides

Disease(s)	Causal Agent(s)	Comments
Acremonium wilt	*Acremonium strictum*	Nearly all hybrids are resistant to this disease. Fungicides are not labeled and should not be used for management.
Anthracnose leaf blight	*Colletotrichum graminicola*	Anthracnose leaf blight occurs early to midway through the season and is most prevalent in southern U.S. production regions. Fungicides are registered for use on this disease, but no yield advantages have been demonstrated with fungicide management.
Bacterial leaf disease complex	*Burkholderia andropogonis, Xanthomonas campestris* pv. *holcicola*	The bacteria that cause this complex of diseases can be seedborne or spread by wind and rain. Most hybrids have adequate levels of resistance. Fungicides are not labeled and should not be used for management.
Bacterial top rot	*Erwinia chrysanthemi*	Bacteria enter plants from splashing rain, from overhead irrigation, or when flood waters rise above the whorl. Symptoms can be confused with those of herbicide injury. Fungicides are not labeled and should not be used for management.
Covered kernel smut	*Sporisorium sorghi*	This disease is rarely seen in commercial production, because it is adequately controlled by seed treatments.
Crazy top	*Sclerophthora macrospora*	Crazy top is observed in fields with early season ponding and excessive moisture. Excellent control can be provided by seed treatments with fungicides that control oomycetes.
Ergot	*Claviceps sorghi*	Infection can occur if the flower has not been fertilized. Fungicides are labeled but typically used only in hybrid seed production fields.
Grain mold and head blight	*Fusarium thapsinum, Curvularia lunata, Colletotrichum graminicola, Alternaria alternata,* others	Grain mold and head blight are most common when rain occurs during flowering. Fungicides are not labeled and should not be used for management.

(continued)

TABLE 18. Continued

Disease(s)	Causal Agent(s)	Comments
Gray leaf spot	*Cercospora sorghi*	This mid- to late-season disease (Fig. 83) is favored by cloudy, humid weather. Fungicides are registered for use, but no yield advantages have been demonstrated by fungicide management.
Head smut	*Sporisorium reilianum*	Head smut is observed infrequently in commercial production. Fungicides are not available for use.
Ladder leaf spot	*Cercospora fusimaculans*	This disease occurs in Georgia and Texas but only rarely. Fungicides are registered for use, but no yield advantages have been demonstrated by fungicide management.
Nematode diseases	Several	Several nematodes can cause diseases in sorghum, but the causal agents differ by region. Fungicides are not labeled for management and should not be used for these diseases.
Northern leaf blight	*Exserohilum turcicum*	Most hybrids have adequate resistance to this disease. Although fungicides are registered for use, no yield advantages have been demonstrated with fungicide management.
Pokkah Boeng (Twisted top)	*Fusarium* spp.	So-called twisted top occurs following prolonged periods of wet weather. Fungicides are not labeled and should not be used for management.
Root and seedling blights	*Fusarium* spp., *Pythium* spp., *Rhizoctonia* spp., others	Multiple fungi and oomycetes can cause seedling blight and stand issues. Seed treatments are applied to manage both seedborne and soilborne pathogens.
Rough leaf spot	*Ascochyta sorghina*	This disease may develop during wet years in fields where sorghum is grown continuously for several years. Fungicides are not labeled and should not be used for management.
Rust	*Puccinia purpurea*	Rust is a late-season disease (Fig. 84) and most common in southern U.S. production areas. Fungicides are available, but yield loss rarely occurs from this disease.
Sooty stripe	*Ramulispora sorghi*	Many hybrids have adequate levels of resistance to sooty stripe, but the disease is a serious problem on susceptible hybrids during years with frequent rainfall. Fungicides are not labeled and should not be used for management.

Fig. 83. Gray leaf spot on sorghum. (Courtesy Casey Schleicher)

Fig. 84. Rust on sorghum. (Courtesy Doug Jardine)

(continued)

TABLE 18. Continued

Disease(s)	Causal Agent(s)	Comments
Sorghum downy mildew	*Peronosclerospora sorghi*	This disease is observed in fields with early season ponding and excessive moisture. Adequate resistance is available in some hybrids. Seed treatments with fungicides that control oomycetes can provide excellent control.
Stalk rots	*Fusarium* spp., *Macrophomina phaseolina*	Sorghum is susceptible to fewer stalk rots than corn, but heat and moisture stress and other production factors can influence the severity of these rots. If foliar diseases are present and being treated with fungicides, the severity of stalk rots may be reduced, as well. Seed treatments have no effect.
Viruses	Several	Several viruses can cause diseases in sorghum, and the symptoms may be confused with those of fungal diseases. Virus diseases differ by region. Fungicides are not labeled for management and should not be used for these diseases.
Zonate leaf spot	*Gloeocercospora sorghi*	This leaf spot disease occurs occasionally during wet years, and most hybrids have adequate resistance to it. Fungicides are registered for use on this disease, but fungicide management has not demonstrated any yield advantages.

Soybean

Foliar Fungicides

Many fungal diseases on soybean can be managed using a combination of practices, including resistant cultivars, crop rotation, tillage, and foliar fungicides. The use of foliar fungicides has increased in recent years, in part because of the introduction of soybean rust (Fig. 85) to the United States in 2004 and the increase in soybean prices.

The decision to apply a fungicide to manage a disease should be based on an increased risk of the disease developing (for instance, soybean rust or white mold) or actual disease identification, as well as the developmental stage at which the disease occurs and the current and forecasted weather. Other factors to consider before applying a foliar fungicide include these:

- Cultivars of soybean differ in their susceptibility to fungal diseases.

Fig. 85. Rust on soybean. (Courtesy Daren S. Mueller)

- Cropping history and the percentage of surface crop residue both affect the risk of disease. Many pathogens survive in residue, which can be a source of inoculum.
- Development of many fungal diseases is favored by humid or wet weather.
- Disease that is present in the early reproductive growth stages may result in greater yield loss than disease that occurs later, during pod fill.
- Fungicides do not have activity against bacterial diseases, such as bacterial blight and bacterial pustule.
- Ground applications during the reproductive growth stages may reduce yields by 2–3 bushels per acre (135–202 kg/ha) because of the effects of wheel traffic through the field.
- The profitability of a fungicide application depends on the yield potential, the price of soybeans, and the cost of application.

Foliar fungicides are typically applied only once during the season, if at all. However, additional applications may be needed to achieve acceptable control of certain fungal diseases. Several factors may influence the number of applications needed:

- the stage of crop development when disease first appears
- the incidence and severity of foliar fungal diseases, as determined by crop scouting
- the current and forecasted weather conditions
- the yield potential of the crop
- the price of soybeans
- the cost of application

The timing of application is critical to maximize the effectiveness of the fungicides and will depend on the target disease. For example, if the target disease is white mold, then making applications during flowering is critical, whereas for most other diseases, protecting the plant during pod fill is most critical.

The onset of the disease will also influence timing. For soybean rust, early detection is critical to successful management. Detection and monitoring tools exist, including the national Soybean Rust ipmPIPE website.[1] Fungicides must be applied in the early stages of a soybean rust epidemic (from preinfection

---

[1] Go to http://sbr.ipmpipe.org

to less than 5% incidence on leaves in the lower canopy) to be highly effective. Control of any disease may be severely compromised if applications are made well before infection occurs in a field or after the disease has been firmly established.

Seed Treatments

Fungicide seed treatments for soybean have also increased in recent years. Many commercial seed treatment facilities can provide at least two different fungicide modes of action that are effective against fungi (including *Fusarium* and *Rhizoctonia* species) and oomycetes (including *Pythium* and *Phytophthora* species).

Fungicide seed treatments are most effective under the following conditions:

- early planting in cold, wet soils
- planting in reduced-till and no-till fields
- planting seed with a low germination rate (less than 80%) or low seed vigor
- planting at a low seeding population

TABLE 19. Soybean diseases and their responses to fungicides

Disease(s)	Causal Agent(s)	Comments
Aerial blight	*Rhizoctonia solani*	Aerial blight occurs primarily in the southern United States. Foliar fungicides can be effective in management, but resistance to quinone outside inhibitor (QoI) fungicides has been reported in some areas.
Anthracnose stem blight	*Colletotrichum* spp.	Disease that develops during the early to middle reproductive stages may require a fungicide application. Foliar fungicides are not needed to treat late-season symptoms, although some products are labeled for management.
Bacterial blight	*Pseudomonas syringae*	Bacterial blight is a common foliar disease throughout the north-central United States and the contiguous Canadian provinces, and it may be confused with brown spot or soybean rust. Fungicides are not labeled and should not be used for management.
Bacterial pustule	*Xanthomonas axonopodis* pv. *glycines*	Bacterial pustule develops middle to late season, when temperatures are warm, and it may be confused with soybean rust. Fungicides are not labeled and should not be used for management.
Brown stem rot	*Phialophora gregata* (*Cadophora gregata*)	This can be an economically important disease throughout the north-central United States and contiguous Canadian provinces. The most effective means of management is the use of resistant cultivars. Foliar fungicide applications and seed treatments are not effective against this disease.
Cercospora leaf blight	*Cercospora kikuchii*	Yield losses from Cercospora leaf blight (Fig. 86, page 90) are common, especially in the southern United States. This disease is often suppressed with foliar fungicides, but several applications may be needed. Fungicides are not effective if infection occurs during the vegetative stages. Resistance to QoI fungicides has been reported in some areas.
Charcoal rot	*Macrophomina phaseolina*	Symptoms of charcoal rot appear in hot, dry weather, when unfavorable environmental conditions stress the plant. This disease is not affected by foliar fungicide applications or seed treatments.
Downy mildew	*Peronospora manshurica*	Downy mildew is a common foliar disease of soybean but seldom causes serious yield losses. No foliar fungicides are labeled for its management. Fungicide seed treatments can prevent initial transmission when seed is infected but will not prevent spores from outside sources from infecting plants at later stages of growth.

[a] Information about the current distribution of soybean rust and how to determine risk at a specific location is available on the web page of the U.S. Department of Agriculture Soybean Rust ipmPIPE (http://sbr.ipmpipe.org).

(continued)

TABLE 19. Continued

Disease(s)	Causal Agent(s)	Comments
Frogeye leaf spot	*Cercospora sojina*	Frogeye leaf spot (Fig. 87) is a common foliar disease that is especially problematic in continuously planted soybean fields. Resistant cultivars are available, but foliar fungicides are commonly applied. Resistance to QoI fungicides has been reported in some areas.
Fusarium root rot	*Fusarium* spp.	*Fusarium* species are common soil fungi, but the economic impact of the root rot they cause is not well documented. Several seed treatments are effective, but foliar fungicides are not.
Nematode diseases	Soybean cyst nematode (SCN) (*Heterodera glycines*), several others	SCN is the most important pathogen of soybean. However, several other nematodes can also cause yield losses, depending on their populations in the field; the causal agents differ by region. Fungicides are not labeled and should not be used for management of these diseases.
Phomopsis seed rot	*Phomopsis longicolla*	This seed rot disease may affect seed germination and seedling vigor. Seed treatments with fungicides may reduce seedling infection, and foliar fungicide applications in the middle to late reproductive stages may reduce seed infection.
Phytophthora root rot	*Phytophthora sojae*	This economically important disease is most severe in poorly drained soils. Plants with disease symptoms often occur singly or in patches in low-lying areas of fields. Phytophthora root rot is best managed by planting resistant cultivars. Seed treatments with metalaxyl and mefenoxam can provide some protection against the causal agent.
Pod and stem blight	*Diaporthe phaseolorum* var. *sojae*	Applications of foliar fungicides may protect seed quality but not affect yield. Disease levels are often not severe enough to warrant fungicide applications. Seed treatments are not effective for this stage of the disease. (See also the discussion of stem canker.)

Fig. 86. Cercospora leaf blight on soybean. (Courtesy Daren S. Mueller)

Fig. 87. Frogeye leaf spot on soybean. (Courtesy Daren S. Mueller)

(continued)

TABLE 19. Continued

Disease(s)	Causal Agent(s)	Comments
Powdery mildew	*Microsphaera manshurica*	Powdery mildew, which is most prevalent in cool conditions, is an uncommon disease on soybean. Even so, yield losses can be noticeable when the disease develops. Several foliar fungicides are effective for management.
Pythium root rot	*Pythium* spp.	Pythium root rot is primarily a seedling disease. Seed treatments with metalaxyl and mefenoxam can provide some protection, but resistance has been documented to both.
Rhizoctonia root rot	*Rhizoctonia solani*	Rhizoctonia root rot is a common soilborne disease that causes reddish-brown lesions on the hypocotyls at the soil line. Several seed treatments are effective; foliar fungicides are not.
Septoria brown spot	*Septoria glycines*	Septoria brown spot is the most common foliar disease of soybean. The disease develops soon after planting and is usually present throughout the growing season. Yield losses depend on how far up the canopy the disease progresses during grain fill. Foliar application of fungicides may be necessary if the disease moves up the canopy during the early to middle reproductive growth stages.
Southern blight	*Sclerotium rolfsii*	Southern blight, which is characterized by white fungal growth on stems near the soil line, is a minor disease in the southern United States. Fungicides are not effective against this disease.
Soybean rust	*Phakopsora pachyrhizi*	Soybean rust is an aggressive disease capable of causing defoliation and significant yield losses. Application of foliar fungicides may be necessary if the risk for this disease is high.[a] The pathogen will not survive in northern growing areas.
Stem canker	*Diaporthe* spp.	There are two similar but distinct stem canker diseases. Northern stem canker is prevalent in northern regions of the United States. Southern stem canker is prevalent in the southern regions but has also been reported in some northern states. Fungicide seed treatments may reduce levels of these diseases, but no foliar fungicides are available.
Sudden death syndrome	*Fusarium virguliforme*	Sudden death syndrome is a very common soilborne disease. No foliar or seed treatment fungicides are currently available, but seed treatments are expected to be available in the future.
Viruses	Several	Several viruses can cause diseases in soybean, and the symptoms may be confused with those of fungal diseases. Virus diseases differ by region. Insecticide seed treatments may affect the insect vectors of certain viruses, but seed treatments do not affect virus diseases. Fungicides are not labeled and should not be used for management.
White mold	*Sclerotinia sclerotiorum*	White mold is prevalent in cool growing regions and can cause significant yield losses, especially during cool, wet seasons. Foliar fungicides can effectively manage white mold or at least reduce disease severity, but the timing of applications is critical. Applications made during flowering are more effective than those made during later reproductive stages.

Sugar Beet

Foliar Fungicides

Generally, the best approach to disease management for sugar beet is an integrated system that includes rotation of tolerant cultivars with nonhost crops, tillage, and timely fungicide applications. Foliar fungicides are typically applied to control the fungal pathogens that cause foliar diseases such as Cercospora leaf spot and soilborne diseases such as crown and root rot.

Cercospora leaf spot occurs after row closure under warm and humid or wet conditions (Fig. 88). Scouts should begin looking for symptoms in fields planted with the most susceptible cultivars, as well as those close to waterways, next to windrows, and adjacent to fields that had diseased sugar beet crops the previous year. The first fungicide application should be made at the onset of disease or when the disease threshold is reached for a specific time of the season.

Subsequent applications should be made based on the presence of symptoms and favorable environmental conditions.

Foliar applications can be made aerially or by ground rig. Aerial applicators should use a minimum of 5 gallons of water per acre (47 L/ha), and areas under power lines and next to trees should be spot treated so they will not serve as sources of inoculum. Ground applicators should use 20 gallons of water per acre (187 L/ha) and a pressure of 100 pounds per square inch (689 kPa) for best control. Effective fungicides with different modes of action may be used individually at full rates in rotation or in mixtures at 75% the full labeled rates in a rotation system to avoid developing fungicide-resistant isolates.

The major soilborne pathogen that can be controlled with fungicides is *Rhizoctonia solani* (Fig. 89), which causes damping-off and crown and root rot. In-furrow fungicide application will provide protection against damping-off when soils are wet and warm at planting. Most years, plants are in the four- to six-leaf growth stage when the average temperature at a soil depth of 4 inches (10 cm) is 65°F (18°C), which is the temperature required for infection to begin. Fungicides must be applied before infection occurs to provide control. In a field with a history of root rot, fungicides should be applied before the average soil temperature at the 4-inch (10-cm) depth reaches 65°F (18°C), irrespective of plant size. Both

Fig. 88. Cercospora leaf spot on sugar beet. (Courtesy Mohamed Khan)

Fig. 89. Foliar symptoms of Rhizoctonia root rot on sugar beet. (Courtesy Mohamed Khan)

in-furrow and foliar applications in a 7-inch (18-cm) T-band of fungicides are typically recommended and provide effective control. T-band application is similar to in-furrow application but with an additional band applied across the top of the furrow. If band applicators are not available, broadcasting the most effective fungicide at its highest labeled rate is recommended.

There have been reports of phytotoxicity when fungicides have been mixed with starter fertilizers and other pesticides. It is best to apply fungicides alone.

Seed Treatments

Sugar beet seed is treated with thiram and metalaxyl or mefenoxam fungicides. Both fungicides provide control against *Pythium* species. Thiram is a contact fungicide, so it is limited to treating *Pythium* infections very early after planting; it is also effective against *Rhizoctonia* species.

Hymexazol may be applied to pelleted seed at 0.8–1.8 ounces (20–45 g) per 100,000 seeds to provide early season protection against Aphanomyces damping-off.

TABLE 20. Sugar beet diseases and their responses to fungicides

Disease(s)	Causal Agent(s)	Comments
Alternaria leaf spot	*Alternaria alternata, A. brassicae*	Alternaria leaf spot is observed infrequently and generally not of economic importance. Foliar fungicides are effective against this disease but not typically recommended for use, since it does not often cause economic loss.
Bacterial leaf spot	*Pseudomonas syringae* pv. *aptata*	Bacterial leaf spot occurs early in the season and is commonly observed after heavy winds and wet conditions. The symptoms of this disease can be confused with those of Cercospora leaf spot. Symptoms disappear under warm, dry conditions, and economic loss typically does not result. Fungicides are not labeled and should not be used for management.
Cercospora leaf spot	*Cercospora beticola*	Cercospora leaf spot is the most common and important foliar disease on sugar beet. The fungus survives in crop residue. Integration of tolerant cultivars, crop rotation, and timely fungicide application are the most effective management strategies. This disease may cause significant economic loss if not controlled. Resistance to many fungicides has been reported in the United States and Europe.
Damping-off	*Pythium aphanidermatum*	This disease is infrequently observed. Fungicide seed treatments typically provide protection.
Damping-off, crown and root rot	*Rhizoctonia solani*	This is the most widespread and important soilborne disease on sugar beet. The pathogen can cause disease in dry or wet conditions in warm soils. In-furrow fungicide applications will prevent damping-off. Good control against crown and root rot can be achieved with band (7-inch [17.75-cm]) application of effective fungicides just before infection is likely to occur.
Damping-off, root rot	*Aphanomyces cochlioides*	This causal agent is active in wet and warm conditions. Damping-off may be prevented with a seed treatment, but this treatment will not provide season-long protection. Tolerant cultivars, along with seed treatment, should be used in fields with a history of the disease.
Nematode diseases	Several	Several nematodes can cause diseases in sugar beet, but the causal agents differ by region. No effective, economical nematicides are available for use on sugar beet. Tolerant cultivars are available, but they tend to be more susceptible to Cercospora leaf spot. Fields planted with nematode-tolerant cultivars should be scouted and treated first for the *Cercospora* pathogen. Fungicides are not labeled and should not be used for management.
Phoma leaf spot	*Phoma betae*	Foliar symptoms may be observed in sugar beets grown for roots. Fungicides are not labeled for foliar application and should not be used for management. Fungicide seed treatments typically control this pathogen.

(continued)

TABLE 20. Continued

Disease(s)	Causal Agent(s)	Comments
Powdery mildew	*Erysiphe polygoni*	Sulfur, demethylation inhibitor (DMI), and quinone outside inhibitor (QoI) fungicides provide effective control of powdery mildew. Fungicide applications should start at the onset of disease, especially when infection occurs early in the season (Fig. 90).
Viruses	Several	Several viruses can cause diseases in sugar beet (such as rhizomania), and the symptoms may be confused with those of fungal diseases. Virus diseases differ by region. Fungicides are not labeled for management and should not be used for these diseases.
Yellows	*Fusarium oxysporum*, *Verticillium albo-atrum*, *V. dahliae*	No fungicides currently provide effective control of Fusarium yellows on sugar beet. Tolerant cultivars should be selected in areas with a history of this disease. Verticillium yellows has been reported where potato is grown in rotation with sugar beet, but this disease is not considered a major problem.

Fig. 90. Powdery mildew on sugar beet. (Courtesy Mohamed Khan)

Sunflower

Foliar Fungicides

The most important sunflower disease that can be managed by applying foliar fungicides is rust (Fig. 91). With some exceptions, if the average disease severity of rust on the upper four leaves of a plant reaches 1% at or before the R5 stage (bloom), then a single foliar fungicide application at that time is recommended and will sufficiently manage the disease. If the onset of rust occurs in the vegetative growth stages, then multiple applications may be necessary. Fungicides are not recommended for rust control after flowering is complete (R6 growth stage or later).

Fungicide applications may provide effective control of other foliar fungal and stem diseases, but only limited data are available on application technology, timing, and economic return. Fungicides are used successfully in Europe for management of Phomopsis stem canker. However, in the United States, fungicide recommendations are limited because of the lack of data on the effectiveness of currently labeled products and on application timing.

Research on the management of diseases with fungicides is ongoing. As new chemicals are labeled or a pathogen (such as *Plasmopara halstedii,* which causes downy mildew) becomes resistant to available fungicides, recommendations may change. This is particularly true for sunflower—a crop with few labeled fungicides and a limited research base on fungicide effectiveness and application timing. Additionally, some evidence from other regions, such as Europe, suggests that management of diseases with fungicides may be possible if additional products are labeled and timing strategies in the U.S. environment are determined. It is important to consult the latest fungicide recommendations when considering fungicides for disease management.

Seed Treatments

The most important sunflower disease that can be managed with seed treatments is downy mildew (Fig. 92). Historically, mefenoxam and metalaxyl have been used widely and effectively. However, pathogen resistance to these fungicides was reported in 1999 in North America, and their chemistries are no longer considered useful. Seed treatments using quinone outside inhibitors (QoIs) are available and widely used for the management and suppression of downy mildew.

With rare exceptions, all sunflower seed is sold with a fungicide seed treatment. In addition to managing and suppressing downy mildew, seed treatment combinations are used with modes of action that manage fungi (such as *Fusarium* species) and oomycetes (such as *Pythium* species).

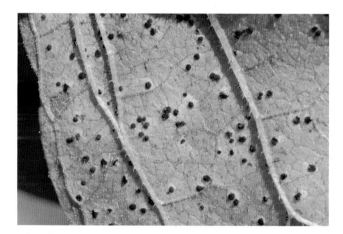

Fig. 91. Rust on sunflower. (Courtesy Samuel Markell)

Fig. 92. Downy mildew on sunflower. (Courtesy Samuel Markell)

TABLE 21. Sunflower diseases and their responses to fungicides

Disease(s)	Causal Agent(s)	Comments
Alternaria leaf spot	*Alternaria* spp.	This disease is common in North America and develops primarily during the late growth stages. Although yield losses from the disease are rare, they have been documented on other continents when infection has occurred early and conditions have remained warm and humid. In those situations, fungicide use was effective at reducing the disease and provided an economic return.
Apical chlorosis	*Pseudomonas syringae* pv. *tagetis*	Apical chlorosis is a striking disease that causes bleaching of leaves, giving infected plants a glowing appearance. Plants grow out of the disease, and yield losses are minimal. Fungicides are not labeled and should not be used for management.
Bacterial stalk and head rot	*Erwinia carotovora*	This causal agent can be present in crop residue in many fields following prolonged periods of high moisture, but the disease develops only sporadically on plants. Fungicides are not labeled and should not be used for management.
Botrytis head rot (gray mold)	*Botrytis cinerea*	So-called gray mold occurs under cool, wet growing conditions. Yield losses have been documented but are not commonly observed in North America. Although fungicide control with multiple applications has been demonstrated, it is not considered economical or necessary and is therefore not recommended.
Charcoal rot	*Macrophomina phaseolina*	Charcoal rot occurs infrequently in the northern Great Plains but more commonly in the central and southern regions (the High Plains). It can cause yield losses in an environment of high temperature or water stress. Fungicides are not effective and should not be used.
Downy mildew	*Plasmopara halstedii*	Fungicide seed treatments are effective, economical, and recommended for management of downy mildew. However, resistance to metalaxyl and mefenoxam is widespread, and so these chemicals are not recommended. Foliar fungicides are not effective and should not be used.
Nematode diseases	Several	Several nematodes can cause diseases in sunflower; the causal agents differ by region. Whether nematodes cause yield losses in sunflower in North America is unclear. Fungicides are not labeled and should not be used for management.
Phoma black stem	*Phoma macdonaldii*	This is one of the most widespread diseases on sunflower in North America, but it is not considered economically important. It is unclear whether fungicides can reduce levels of this disease, and they are not recommended for use.
Phomopsis stem canker	*Diaporthe helianthi*, *D. gulyae*	Localized disease outbreaks with severe yield losses have occurred in the northern Great Plains. Yield losses are common in Europe, and fungicides are routinely used there for disease management. Fungicides can be useful for disease management in the United States and Canada; the evaluation of available chemicals and application timing is ongoing.
Powdery mildew	*Golovinomyces cichoracearum*	Powdery mildew is a relatively common disease on leaves as plants approach maturity. Yield losses are rare but have been documented. The application of foliar fungicides can reduce the level of disease but is unlikely to be economical.
Rhizopus head rot	*Rhizopus arrhizus*, *R. stolonifer*	This disease is common in the High Plains but relatively rare in the northern Great Plains. Head rot is often associated with injury (from hail, insects, birds, etc.). Management is accomplished primarily by controlling the sunflower head moth.

(continued)

TABLE 21. Continued

Disease(s)	Causal Agent(s)	Comments
Rust	*Puccinia helianthi*	Rust is a common disease that may reduce yield, particularly when the level of severity on upper leaves reaches 1% at or before R5 (bloom). Fungicides are effective and can be used to manage rust.
Sclerotinia diseases (head rot, stalk rot, and wilt)	*Sclerotinia sclerotiorum*	The *Sclerotinia* pathogen and the diseases it causes are widespread. Although each disease phase is of economic concern, fungicide efficacy has not been consistently demonstrated and is not recommended.
Septoria leaf spot	*Septoria helianthi, S. helianthina*	This disease occurs commonly in North America but rarely causes economic concern. It frequently develops on the lower leaves and late in the growing season. Fungicide applications may be effective on Septoria leaf spot but are not likely economically viable.
Southern blight (collar rot)	*Sclerotium rolfsii*	In North America, this disease has been identified only in the southern United States, and significant yield losses have been rare. Fungicide seed treatments may help manage seedling death but are unlikely to manage collar rot.
Verticillium wilt, Verticillium leaf mottle	*Verticillium dahliae*	These diseases occur commonly in North America and may cause yield losses. Infection occurs through the roots and causes wilting. Fungicides are not recommended.
Viruses	Several	Several viral pathogens are known to infect sunflower, and the symptoms may be confused with those of fungal diseases. Virus diseases are considered rare, however, and they differ by region. Fungicides are not labeled and should not be used for management.
White rust	*Albugo tragopogonis*	White rust occurs rarely in North America but is considered a serious disease in other countries, such as South Africa and Argentina, where significant yield losses have occurred. The effectiveness and economics of foliar fungicide applications are unclear.

Tobacco

Foliar- and Soil-Applied Fungicides

A number of tobacco diseases can be managed effectively with foliar- and soil-applied fungicides, particularly when combined with sound management practices (such as crop rotation and sanitation) and

Fig. 93. Pythium root rot on tobacco transplants. (Courtesy Kenneth Seebold)

resistant cultivars. These elements form the basis of an integrated disease management program that can minimize losses in yield and leaf quality, thereby increasing overall profitability for the tobacco farmer.

Knowing when to apply fungicides is important to achieving maximum performance and economic return. The correct time depends on the product to be used, the disease to be controlled, the environmental conditions, and the history of a given disease in the field.

A disease that occurs during transplant production can cause heavy losses and be difficult to control once an epidemic has developed (Fig. 93). To reduce the risk of a severe outbreak of disease, fungicide application should be considered before symptoms appear. For Pythium root rot, the water should be treated in a hydroponic system ("float bed") when roots begin to emerge from tray bottoms, and follow-up applications should be made on a 14- to 21-day schedule as needed. To prevent target spot and blue mold (Fig. 94), applications of fungicide should begin when plants are large enough to clip or mow and continue on a 5- to 7-day schedule until transplanting.

Regular scouting for foliar diseases on tobacco is necessary to assess disease levels and then determine when fungicide applications should begin. Current management guidelines for foliar diseases recommend the following:

- Make at least one application of fungicide if target spot is present on seedlings at transplanting.

Fig. 94. Target spot (left) and blue mold (right) on tobacco. (Courtesy Kenneth Seebold)

- If a field has a history of target spot or frogeye leaf spot or if either disease is observed on plants in the first few weeks after transplanting, then treat at layby (last cultivation) or before the crop canopy closes. Also make follow-up applications, if needed.
- Apply fungicides for blue mold when crop reports indicate a threat exists in the region.
- When a fungicide is applied after canopy closure, use of a drop nozzle may be required to achieve the coverage necessary for optimal performance.

Field and cropping history are important factors for black shank and other soilborne diseases. In general, land rotated away from tobacco for 1 year or more is less prone to outbreaks of black shank, Fusarium wilt (Fig. 95), and black root rot. The chances are greater of encountering these diseases in fields where they have occurred previously. The likelihood of this scenario requires planting resistant cultivars and using a soil-applied fungicide, in the case of black shank. Some fields have a history of high foliar disease severity. Fields that are located in river bottoms or low areas or that are surrounded by trees may be more prone to damage from blue mold, target spot, and frogeye leaf spot.

The development of most foliar diseases on tobacco is favored by wet weather and moderate to warm temperatures (70–80°F [21–27°C]). In contrast, blue mold is favored by cool (60°F [16°C]) and humid conditions.

The pathogen that causes blue mold (*Peronospora tabacina*) typically does not overwinter in production areas where frosts or freezes occur. Instead, *P. tabacina* is introduced when windborne spores move from production areas or wild tobacco south of the temperate zone or on transplants produced in areas where blue mold is active much of the year. Thus, fungicides are not always required for blue mold and should be applied only when the disease is nearby or threatens an area. Local extension specialists can provide the current status of blue mold, and information is also available from the North American Plant Disease Forecast Center.[1]

To avoid severe plant injury, tobacco fungicides should never be used with adjuvants or tank mixed with growth regulators (sucker controls). Some fungicides are not compatible with emulsifiable concentrate (EC) formulations of pesticides. Farmers and applicators should check labels carefully before tank mixing a fungicide with any product.

Seed Treatments

Although tobacco seedlings can be attacked by soilborne pathogens such as *Pythium* and *Rhizoctonia* species, tobacco seed is not treated with fungicides. Treatment of tobacco seed is impractical because of its small size. Also, most transplants produced in the United States are grown in a peat-based substrate at a small- or large-scale hydroponic facility, reducing the threat from soilborne pathogens during germination and thus eliminating the need for seed treatment.

Fig. 95. Fusarium wilt on tobacco. (Courtesy Kenneth Seebold)

---

[1] Go to www.ces.ncsu.edu/depts/pp/bluemold

TABLE 22. Tobacco diseases and their responses to fungicides

Disease(s)	Causal Agent(s)	Comments
Angular leaf spot	*Pseudomonas syringae* pv. *tabaci*	Angular leaf spot is a bacterial disease that can be seedborne. Copper products and agricultural streptomycin are labeled for management, but routine use is generally not necessary. Fungicides are not labeled and should not be used for management.
Anthracnose	*Colletotrichum destructivum*	Anthracnose is a sporadic problem in transplant production. Mancozeb products can be applied to suppress this disease.
Black root rot	*Thielaviopsis basicola*	This soilborne disease is most problematic when soil temperatures are cool. It can be controlled by using resistant cultivars and cultural practices.
Black shank	*Phytophthora nicotianae*	Black shank is a destructive soilborne disease that is most severe in warm climates. Mefenoxam and metalaxyl fungicides are labeled for soil treatment and should be used in conjunction with cultural practices and resistant cultivars.
Blue mold	*Peronospora tabacina*	This foliar disease occurs only sporadically but can be highly destructive. The causal agent generally does not overwinter in temperate areas but spreads via wind from sites where cultivated or wild tobacco survives year-round. Foliar fungicides are labeled and needed to prevent losses during outbreaks of blue mold. Cultivars are available with partial resistance to the disease.
Brown spot	*Alternaria alternata*	Brown spot is a common foliar disease that can damage maturing tobacco in wet years. No fungicides are labeled for management of this disease.
Collar rot	*Sclerotinia sclerotiorum*	This disease is encountered primarily during the production of transplants. Recommended controls include sanitation, fertility management, and adequate ventilation in production facilities. No fungicides are labeled for management of collar rot.
Damping-off	*Pythium* spp., *Rhizoctonia solani*	Damping-off is most likely to occur during transplant production, but it may also affect newly transplanted seedlings. The pathogens can overwinter in transplant trays, making sanitation a key management strategy. Mancozeb is labeled as a foliar spray for suppression of Rhizoctonia damping-off.
Frogeye leaf spot	*Cercospora nicotianae*	This disease may affect tobacco at any growth stage but is found most commonly on maturing leaves. Severe outbreaks can occur during wet, warm seasons. Azoxystrobin is labeled and likely needed under conditions that favor disease, but it is important to monitor for fungicide resistance.
Fusarium wilt	*Fusarium oxysporum* f. sp. *nicotianae*	Fusarium wilt is a soilborne disease that can be difficult to manage because of the pathogen's persistent nature in soils. Management strategies include sanitation, crop rotation, and planting resistant varieties. Soil fumigants can be applied prior to planting and may be needed in areas with high disease pressure or nematode problems.
Granville wilt	*Pseudomonas solanacearum*	This bacterial disease is common on tobacco grown in North and South Carolina. Cultural practices and resistant cultivars are recommended for management. Soil fumigation may be a valuable part of an integrated pest management program. Fungicides are not labeled and should not be used for management.
Hollow stalk	*Erwinia carotovora* subsp. *carotovora*, *E. carotovora* subsp. *atroseptica*	Hollow stalk is a bacterial disease and can be suppressed somewhat using sanitation and cultural practices. Fungicides are not labeled and should not be used for management.
Nematode diseases	Several	Several nematodes can cause diseases in tobacco, but the causal agents differ by region. Fungicides are not labeled for management and should not be used for these diseases.

(continued)

TABLE 22. Continued

Disease(s)	Causal Agent(s)	Comments
Pythium root rot	*Pythium* spp.	Pythium root rot develops during transplant production. The fungicide etridiazole is labeled for use in hydroponic systems and should be applied preventively as a routine practice.
Sore shin	*Rhizoctonia solani*	This disease develops within a few weeks of transplanting. Monitoring for symptoms and applying cultural practices can reduce the incidence of this disease. No fungicides are labeled for use on sore shin.
Target spot	*Thanatephorus cucumeris*	Target spot causes significant losses during transplant production and in the field following periods of overcast or rainy weather. Foliar fungicides are labeled for use on this disease, and applications are required when environmental conditions favor disease development.
Viruses	Several	Several viruses can cause diseases in tobacco, and the symptoms may be confused with those of fungal diseases. Virus diseases differ by region. Fungicides are not labeled for management and should not be used for these diseases.

Bibliography

Bardas, G. A., Veloukas, T., Koutita, O., and Karaoglanidis, S. 2010. Multiple resistance of *Botrytis cinerea* from kiwifruit to SDHIs, QoIs and fungicides of other chemical groups. Pest Manag. Sci. 66:967-973.

Coakley, S. M., Scherm, H., and Chakraborty, S. 1999. Climate change and plant disease management. Annu. Rev. Phytopathol. 37:399-426.

Dorrance, A. E., Hershman, D. E., and Draper, M. A. 2007. Using Foliar Fungicides to Manage Soybean Rust. North Central Education/Extension Research Activities (NCERA) Committee (NCERA-208) and the Ontario Ministry of Agriculture and Food (OMAF).

Edwards, W., Smith, D., McLees, B., and Baitinger, J. 2000. Ag Decision Maker: 2000 Iowa Farm Custom Rate Survey. Iowa State University, University Extension FM 1698 (Revised). Available online at www.extension.iastate.edu/Publications/ FM1698X00.pdf

Edwards, W., Johanns, A., and Chamra, A. 2011. Ag Decision Maker: 2011 Iowa Farm Custom Rate Survey. Iowa State University, University Extension FM 1698 (Revised). Available online at www.extension.iastate.edu/sites/www.extension. iastate.edu/files/wright/2011CustomRates.pdf

Fungicide Resistance Action Committee (FRAC). 2012. FRAC Code List 2012: Fungicides Sorted by Mode of Action (including FRAC Code numbering). Available online at www.frac.info/frac/publication/anhang/ FRAC-Code-List2011-final.pdf

Hatfield, J., Boote, K., Fay, P., Hahn, L., Izaurralde, C., Kimball, B. A., Mader, T., Morgan, J., Ort, D., Polley, W., Thomson, A., and Wolfe, D. 2008. Agriculture. Pages 21-74 in: The Effects of Climate Change on Agriculture, Land Resources, Water Resources, and Biodiversity, A Report by the U.S. Climate Change Science Program and the Subcommittee on Global Change Research. M. Walsh, ed. U.S. Environmental Protection Agency, Washington, DC.

Hewitt, H. G. 1998. Fungicides in Crop Protection. CAB International, New York.

Johnson, K. B., Johnson, S. B., and Teng, P. S. 1986. Development of a simple potato growth model for use in crop-pest management. Agric. Syst. 19:189-209.

Kim, Y. K., and Xiao, C. L. 2010. Resistance to pyraclostrobin and boscalid in populations of *Botrytis cinerea* from stored apples in Washington State. Plant Dis. 94:604-612.

Krämer, W., and Schirmer, S., eds. 2007. Modern Crop Protection Compounds, vol. 2. Wiley-VCH Verlag, Weinheim, Germany.

Latin, R. 2011. A Practical Guide to Turfgrass Fungicides. American Phytopathological Society, St. Paul, MN.

Lyr, H. 1987. Modern Selective Fungicides: Properties, Applications, Mechanisms of Action. Longman Scientific and Technical, Essex, England.

McMullen, M. P., and Lamey, H. A. 2000. Seed Treatment for Disease Control. North Dakota State University, Extension Bulletin PP-447 (Revised). Available online at www.ag.ndsu.edu/pubs/plantsci/crops/pp447w.htm

Morton, V., and Staub, T. 2008. A Short History of Fungicides. APS*net* Features. doi: 10.1094/ APSnetFeature-2008-0308. Available online at www.apsnet.org/publications/apsnetfeatures/Pages/ Fungicides.aspx

Mueller, D. S., and Bradley, C. A. 2008. Field Crop Fungicides for the North Central United States. North Central IPM Center, Cooperative State Research, Education, and Extension Service (CSREES), U.S. Department of Agriculture, Washington, DC.

North American Plant Disease Forecast Center. n.d. Tobacco Blue Mold Forecast Homepage. North Carolina State University. Available online at www.ces.ncsu.edu/depts/pp/bluemold

U.S. Department of Agriculture. 2007. National Agricultural Statistics Service (NASS). Agricultural Chemical Use Database. Available online at www.pestmanagement.info/nass/app_usage.cfm

U.S. Department of Agriculture. 2010. National Agricultural Statistics Service (NASS). Charts and Maps: Field Crops. Available online at www.nass.usda.gov/Charts_and_Maps/Field_Crops/

Wise, K., and Mueller, D. 2011. Are Fungicides No Longer Just for Fungi? An Analysis of Foliar Fungicide Use in Corn. APS*net* Features. doi:10.1094/APSnetFeature-2011-0531. Available online at www.apsnet.org/publications/apsnetfeatures/Pages/fungicide.aspx

Wise, K. A., Bradley, C. A., Pasche, J. S., and Gudmestad, N. C. 2009. Resistance to QoI fungicides in *Ascochyta rabiei* from chickpea in the northern Great Plains. Plant Dis. 93:528-536.

Zhang, G. R., Newman, M. A., and Bradley, C. A. 2012. First report of the soybean frogeye leaf spot fungus (*Cercospora sojina*) resistant to quinone outside inhibitor fungicides in North America. Plant Dis. 96:767.

Index

breadth of metabolic activity,
  of fungicides, 5, 6
bronzing, and ozone damage, 57
brown root and stem rots
  on alfalfa, 45
  on soybean, 89
brown spot diseases
  on dry beans, 59
  on potato, 69
  on pulse crops, 75
  on rice, 78, 79
  on soybean, 20
  on tobacco, 100
browning and stem break, on flax, 62
Burkholderia
  andropogonis, 85
  glumae, 79

CAA fungicides. *See* carboxylic acid amide
  (CAA) fungicides
Cadophora gregata, 89
canola, 48–49
  diseases of, 48, 49
  foliar fungicides for, 48
  seed treatments for, 12, 48
captan, 30, 33
carbamate fungicides, 33, 39
Carbonum leaf spot, on corn, 52
carboxin, 32
carboxylic acid amide (CAA) fungicides,
  33, 40
carrier volume, 11
CBR. *See* Cylindrocladium black rot
cell wall formation, interference in, 40
Cercospora
  albida, 60
  arachidicola, 67
  beticola, 93
  fusimaculans, 86
  gossypina, 55
  kikuchii, 89
  nicotianae, 100
  oryzae, 79
  sojina, 30, 90
  sorghi, 86
  zeae-maydis, 52
Cercospora diseases
  on corn, 52
  on cotton, 55
  on dry beans, 60
  on peanut, 67
  on rice, 79
  on sorghum, 86
  on soybean, 30, 89, 90
  on sugar beet, 39, 92, 93
  on tobacco, 100
Cercosporidium personatum, 67
C14-demethylase, inhibition of, 37.
    See also demethylation inhibitors
charcoal rot
  on cotton, 55
  on soybean, 89
  on sunflower, 96

chemical groups or classes, of fungicides,
  36–41
  definition of, 6
  examples of, 6
  by FRAC codes, 32–33, 36–41
chemical names, of fungicides, 4
chemigation, 6, 7, 10
chickpea. *See* pulse crops
chloroneb, 32
chlorosis
  of flax, 62
  of sunflower, 96
chlorothalonil, 33, 64, 72
Cladosporium, 82
Clavibacter
  michiganensis
    subsp. *insidiosus*, 45
    subsp. *nebraskensis*, 52
Claviceps
  purpurea, 82
  sorghi, 85
clubroot, of canola, 49
Cochliobolus sativus, 83, 84
collar rot
  of peanut, 67
  of sunflower, 97, 100
Colletotrichum, 89. *See also* anthracnose
    diseases
  coccodes, 69
  destructivum, 100
  graminicola, 51, 53, 85
  lindemuthianum, 58
  lini, 62
  pisi, 74
  trifolii, 45
  truncatum, 72, 74
common bacterial blight, on dry beans, 59
common bunt, on small grains, 12, 81, 82
common leaf spot, on alfalfa, 44, 45
common names, of fungicides, 4
common rust, on corn, 50, 51
common scab, on potato, 70
common smut, on corn, 51
conservation tillage, 18, 55
contact fungicides
  definition of, 5
  introduction of, 30
  washing off of, 5, 23, 41
control plots, in on-farm trials, 25
copper-based products, 30, 33, 57, 100
corn, 50–53
  arrested ear development of, 24, 51
  average price of, 3
  cost of fungicide application for, 16, 17
  crop residue and, 18
  diseases of, 8, 24, 50, 51–53
  foliar fungicides for, 2, 20, 50–51
  hybrids of, 50–51
  seed treatments for, 2, 12, 51
  weather conditions and, 50–51
Corynebacterium insidiosum, 45
Corynespora cassiicola, 55
Corynespora leaf spot, on cotton, 54, 55

costs, of fungicide application, 16, 17.
    See also economic factors
cotton, 54–56
  average price of, 3
  diseases of, 54, 55–56
  foliar fungicides for, 54
  in-furrow and hopper-box treatments
    for, 54
  seed treatments for, 54–55
coverage, of fungicides, 11
covered kernel smut, of sorghum, 85
covered smut, of small grains, 12, 82
crazy top, of sorghum, 51
crop residue, 2–3, 18, 50, 88
crop rotation, 18, 72–73
cross-resistance, to fungicides, 7, 31
crown and root rots
  on alfalfa, 45, 46, 47
  on peanut, 66
  on sugar beet, 92, 93
cultivar selection
  for flax, 61
  for peanut, 66
  risk of disease development and, 17–18
  for small grains, 81
  for soybean, 88
curative activity, 5
Curtobacterium flaccumfaciens pv.
    flaccumfaciens, 59
Curvularia lunata, 85
cyanoacetamide-oxime fungicides, 33, 39
cyazofamid, 33, 38–39
Cylindrocladium black rot (CBR),
    of peanut, 65, 66
Cylindrocladium parasiticum, 66
cymoxanil, 33, 39, 69
cyproconazole, 32
cyprodinil, 32

damping-off
  on alfalfa, 46
  on flax, 62
  on soybean, 37
  on sugar beet, 92, 93
  on tobacco, 100
decision making, for fungicide
    application, 16–28
  for foliar fungicides, 20–24. *See also*
    foliar fungicides
  key factors in, 16–17
  risk of disease development and,
    17–19
  testing via on-farm trials, 25–28
demethylation inhibitor (DMI) fungicides,
  36–37
  effectiveness of, 36
  for Fusarium head blight, 82
  introduction of, 3, 36
  for leaf spots of peanuts, 64–65, 67
  mobility of, 37
  mode of action of, 37
  for powdery mildews, 36, 94
  resistance to, 32

Fusarium diseases
  on alfalfa, 45
  on canola, 48, 49
  on corn, 51, 52, 53
  on cotton, 55, 56
  on dry beans, 58, 59
  on flax, 61, 62
  on peanut, 66, 68
  on potato, 50, 70
  on pulse crops, 75
  on rice, 78, 79
  on small grains, 81, 82, 83, 84
  on sorghum, 85, 86, 87
  on soybean, 89, 90, 91
  on sugar beet, 94
  on sunflower, 95
  on tobacco, 99, 100
  on wheat, 23, 82

Gaeumannomyces graminis, 83
genetic resistance, to disease, 17–18, 81
germ tube growth, inhibition of, 39
Gibberella zeae, 52
Gloeocercospora sorghi, 87
Golovinomyces cichoracearum, 96
Goss's wilt, on corn, 52
grain mold and head blight, on sorghum, 85
Granville wilt, on tobacco, 100
gray leaf spot
  on corn, 8, 50, 52
  on sorghum, 86
gray mold
  on dry beans, 59
  on flax, 62
  on pulse crops, 72–73, 74, 75
  on sunflower, 96
growth regulators, 99

halo blight
  on dry beans, 59
  on sorghum, 85
head blight, on small grains, 23, 82
head molds, on small grains, 82
head rots, on sunflower, 96, 97
head smut
  on corn, 52
  on sorghum, 86
heat and frost cankers, on flax, 63
Helminthosporium solani, 71
herbicides, damage from, 21, 63, 85
heteroaromatic fungicides, 33, 40
Heterodera glycines, 90
Holcus leaf spot, on corn, 52
hollow stalk, on tobacco, 100
hopper-box treatments, 54
Hyaloperonospora parasitica, 49
hydroponic systems, 98, 99
hymexazol, 33, 40, 93

imazalil, 32
in-furrow fungicides
  application of, 7, 13

classes of, 37, 38
  for cotton, 54
  definition of, 7
  for peanut, 66
  for potato, 69
  for sugar beet, 92–93
insecticides, application of, 12
integrated pest management (IPM)
  definition of, 7
  fungicide resistance and, 34
  for peanut, 66
  for potato, 69
IPM. *See* integrated pest management
iprodione, 32
irrigation
  fungicide application through, 6, 10
  management of, 19, 57, 64, 65
  systems of, 6, 10

kernel and false smut, on rice, 78, 79
kickback activity, 5

Lasiodiplodia theobromae, 67
late blight, on potato, 38, 39–40, 69, 70
leaf rust, 83
leaf spot diseases. *See also specific disease names*
  on alfalfa, 44, 45, 46, 47
  on corn, 52
  on cotton, 54, 55
  on dry beans, 58, 60
  on peanut, 64, 65, 67
  on rice, 78, 79
  on sorghum, 87
  on soybean, 30, 90
  on tobacco, 99, 100
least significant difference (LSD), 28
lentil. *See* pulse crops
Leptosphaeria
  biglobosa, 49
  maculans, 49
Leptosphaerulina briosiani, 46
Leptosphaerulina (Lepto) leaf spot, on alfalfa, 46
Leveillula spp., 76
linear chemigation, 10
lipid and membrane synthesis, interference with, 38
loose smut, on small grains, 12, 81, 82
LSD. *See* least significant difference

Macrophomina phaseolina
  on corn, 53
  on cotton, 55
  on dry beans, 58
  on pulse crops, 75
  on sorghum, 87
  on soybean, 89
  on sunflower, 96
Macrophomina root rot, on pulse crops, 75

mancozeb
  multisite activity of, 6, 30, 33
  for potato seed treatment, 69
  for tobacco diseases, 100
mandipropamid, 33
maneb, 33
market prices, of crops. *See also* economic factors
  averages of, 3. *See also specific crop names, subentry* average price of
  increase in fungicide use and, 2, 3
marketing of fungicides, and increase in fungicide use, 2, 3
MBC fungicides. *See* methyl benzimidazole carbamate (MBC) fungicides
mefenoxam
  for alfalfa seed treatment, 46
  resistance to, 30, 32, 95, 95
  for rice seed treatment, 78
  for soybean seed treatment, 90, 91
  for sugar beet seed treatment, 93
  for tobacco soil treatment, 100
Melampsora lini, 63
mercury fungicides, 30
metabolic activity, of fungicides, 5, 6
metalaxyl
  for alfalfa seed treatment, 46
  resistance to, 30, 32, 75, 95, 96
  for rice seed treatment, 78
  for soybean seed treatment, 90, 91
  for sugar beet seed treatment, 93
  for tobacco soil treatment, 100
metconazole, 32
methoxycarbamate, 6
methyl benzimidazole carbamate (MBC) fungicides, 32, 36, 66
metiram, 33
Microdochium nivale, 47
Microsphaera manshurica, 91
microtubule assembly, inhibition of, 39
mineral deficiencies, on flax, 62
mitochondrial respiration, inhibition of, 38
mixing, of fungicide solutions
  correct approach to, 22, 34, 35, 99
  fungicide resistance and, 34
  in tanks, 22, 34, 35, 99
  water used for, 22
  with other products, 93, 99
mobility, of fungicides
  by chemical classes, 36–41
  examples of, 6
  spray coverage/volume and, 11
  by type of fungicide, 5
modes of action, of fungicides
  by chemical classes, 36–41
  definition of, 5–6
  examples of, 5–6
  managing resistance and, 34, 35
moisture
  disease development and, 19, 66
  fungicide application and, 23, 64–65